A GUIDE TO **FORTRAN** PROGRAMMING

McCracken, D. D.

    A Guide to FORTRAN Programming
    A Guide to IBM 1401 Programming
    A Guide to ALGOL Programming
    A Guide to COBOL Programming
    Digital Computer Programming

McCracken, D. D., Weiss, H. and Lee, T. H.

    Programming Business Computers

McCracken, D. D. and Dorn, W. S.

    Numerical Methods and Fortran Programming

DANIEL D. McCRACKEN

McCRACKEN ASSOCIATES, INC.

a guide to
FORTRAN
programming

JOHN WILEY & SONS, INC.

NEW YORK · LONDON · SYDNEY

TWELFTH PRINTING, DECEMBER, 1965

Library of Congress Catalog Card Number: 61–16618

Printed in the United States of America

PREFACE

This book is written for the person who wants to get a rapid grasp of the use of a computer in the solution of problems in science and engineering. The application of a computer to such problems is greatly simplified by the use of FORTRAN or a similar compiler because it is not necessary to learn the details of computer operation. This book presents the essentials of FORTRAN programming in a form that most people can master in a few hours of careful reading and practice.

It is anticipated that the book will be helpful in a variety of situations.

1. It can be used as the text for a one-semester hour course in engineering, science, or mathematics, which provides more than enough time to cover the material. The students can run several practice problems and a sizable term problem. Alternatively, the extra time can be devoted to introducing the students to machine-language programming.

2. It can be used as the text for a supplement to some other course. Covering the fundamentals of FORTRAN will take only a few hours away from the course, and this "lost" time can be recovered by assignments of more realistic problems in the primary subject matter. A particularly happy combination is numerical analysis and FORTRAN programming, by which the time spent in teaching FORTRAN will be more than recovered.

3. Students in an industrial course in FORTRAN programming will find the book useful as an elaboration of the necessarily rather terse descriptions contained in most FORTRAN programming manuals and as a guide to the numerous ways in which FORTRAN can be applied to the solution of realistic problems.

4. The book is also suitable for individual study, either in schools or industry.

In all cases the value of the book is enhanced by the inclusion of graded exercises, with answers to a selected set. Also valuable are the eight case studies, which illustrate the use of FORTRAN in the solution of a variety of problems.

The differences between the various versions of FORTRAN will not be a major problem. It is possible therefore to use the book in conjunction with the manuals of any other version. This question is discussed more fully in the Introduction.

It is a pleasure to acknowledge the many and varied contributions of the following people: Fred Gruenberger and George Armerding of the RAND Corporation; Jack Heller of New York University; Norm Patton and Bill Lee of IBM; Jim Richter and Dick Turner of the General Electric Company; and Bill McGee of Thompson Ramo Wooldridge, Inc. To the many reviewers, unfortunately too numerous to list, my appreciation. Mrs. Elizabeth Plate did most of the typing.

DANIEL D. MCCRACKEN

Ossining, New York
July 1961

CONTENTS

INTRODUCTION: HOW TO USE THIS BOOK EFFECTIVELY

To obtain the most value from a study of this book, the reader should be aware of a few matters concerning its content and organization.

1. There is not just one version of FORTRAN; there are more than a dozen. These differences are in two categories: minor variations in details and fundamental differences in scope. No attempt is made in the text to identify all differences nor to compare the various systems. Instead, the entire presentation is based on FORTRAN for the IBM 709 and 7090, which is the most widely used system and is very nearly the same as FORTRAN for all of the large computers.

The minor details are, in general, not given, in the interest of an orderly and uncluttered exposition. However, Appendix 1 summarizes the characteristics of the various systems. The rather sizable differences in scope are another matter. A number of features of 709 FORTRAN simply do not exist in FORTRAN for such machines as the IBM 650 and 1620. All passages describing large machine features that do not apply to the small machine systems are clearly marked. The reader who is concerned with FORTRAN for a smaller computer is advised at least to skim these passages, but they need not be studied with care.

2. Many examples are used to illustrate the various topics and to show how FORTRAN may be applied effectively. The thing to realize is that these examples do not require knowledge of the field from which they are taken, nor do they require an extensive mathematical background. Anyone with a reasonable grasp of elementary mathematics will understand the mathematical statements of the examples; it is not necessary to understand their physical bases to see how FORTRAN can be valuable in solving the problems.

3. The speed and depth of learning will be enhanced by actual practice in preparing and running programs—early and often. It is of course not *necessary* to have a computer at hand in order to master the subject, but if one is available it should be utilized at every opportunity.

4. Chapter 9, the longest in the book, is devoted to a set of case studies that show how FORTRAN can be used. Some readers will wish to consolidate their knowledge in these studies as they proceed rather than consider all together at the end. Therefore, a note marks each point in the text at which enough background will have been accumulated to make a case study understandable.

1. CONSTANTS, VARIABLES, AND EXPRESSIONS

1.1 What Is FORTRAN?

For an electronic computer to be effective in the solution of an engineering or scientific problem, the problem-solving procedure must be presented to the computer in a language that it can "understand." The computer's basic language consists of elementary *instructions*, such as add, subtract, shift a number right or left, or punch a card. The problem-solving procedure must therefore be *translated* into simple instructions that the computer is capable of obeying. This translation, which is called *programming* or *coding*, can be carried out entirely by a human being, or the computer may assist in the process by use of a *compiler*.

A compiler is a large set of computer instructions which can accept a problem-solving procedure, written in a form resembling the language of the procedure, and produce from it the proper elementary machine instructions that will solve the problem. A compiler that is designed primarily for use in the solution of engineering and scientific problems is generally spoken of as an *algebraic compiler*. The user of an algebraic compiler is not forced to learn the detailed operation of the computer. He is therefore able to concentrate from the outset on the problems to be solved rather than on how the computer operates.

The first widely used algebraic compiler was designed for the IBM 704 by IBM and some of its customers. This system is called FORTRAN, which is a shortened form of FORmula TRANslation. Some of the later versions of FORTRAN, designed for more recent IBM computers or for the computers of other manufacturers, have enlarged the scope of the system to make it more powerful. Other versions have tended in the direction of simplifying the system in order to make it applicable to smaller machines than the IBM 704.

Electronic computers today are widely used to assist in solving the problems of science, engineering, and business. They are used in connection with the design of equipment, in evaluating the results of tests and experiments, in controlling processes, in keeping records of many types, and in a wide variety of applications involving the processing of business data. Their use is based on the ability to operate at great speed, to produce accurate results, to store large quantities of information, and to carry out long and complex sequences of operations without human intervention.

Computer applications can be divided into two broad classifications: scientific and commercial. Commercial work includes such things as payroll, inventory control, sales statistics, production scheduling, and general accounting. Scientific applications include examples such as these.

*The design of equipment often involves so many variables that the evaluation of even one proposed design requires a great deal of work and many proposed designs must be appraised before a production design can be chosen. A computer is extremely valuable in such work, since it can be used to evaluate many combinations of parameters with little additional effort, once the basic procedure has been set up.

*After the over-all design features of a piece of equipment have been established, there often still remains much detailed computation to produce data for shop drawings and instructions. A computer can frequently be used to reduce the drudgery of this phase of the design.

*Laboratory and test-cell experiments often produce so much data that a computer becomes necessary, in order to apply correction factors, to eliminate invalid readings, and to reduce the data to meaningful averages.

The emphasis in this book is on scientific applications, for which FORTRAN is better suited than for commercial applications. This is not to say, however, that FORTRAN cannot be used for commercial work or that the distinction between the two types is always clear-cut.

This book applies to the following compilers, with the reservations noted in the Introduction.

IBM 650 FORTRAN, FORTRANSIT (IBM 650), IBM 1620 FORTRAN, GOTRAN (IBM 1620), IBM 1401 FORTRAN, IBM 704 FORTRAN, IBM 709-7090 FORTRAN, IBM 705 FORTRAN, IBM 7070 FORTRAN, Honeywell Algebraic Compiler (Honeywell 800), ALTAC (Philco 2000), and the FORTRAN-compatible compiler for the Control Data Corporation 1604.

1.2 A FORTRAN Program

A procedure to be followed in solving a problem with FORTRAN is specified by a series of *statements*. These statements are of several types. One type specifies the arithmetic operations that are the heart of the procedure. A second calls for input or output, such as reading a data card, printing a line of results, or punching a card of results. A third specifies the *flow of control* through the set of statements, that is, the sequence in which the statements are to be executed. The fourth consists of statements that provide certain information *about* the procedure without themselves causing any action.

Taken together, all of the statements that specify the manner in which a problem is to be solved

constitute the *source program*. When a source program has been written and punched onto cards, it is translated by FORTRAN into an *object program*, which is a set of the elementary instructions that the computer can understand. The object program is then executed by the computer to solve the problem.

Our task is to investigate each of the FORTRAN statements and to determine how to go about combining them to solve representative problems in science and engineering.

1.3 Constants

We begin by considering the two kinds of numbers that can be used in FORTRAN: *fixed point* and *floating point*.

A fixed point number is just an ordinary integer (whole number). It may be zero or any positive or negative number less than 32768.* Because fixed point numbers can take on only integral values, they are ordinarily used in special situations, as we shall see later.

Most numbers used in a FORTRAN computation are in floating point form. This is a method of representation similar to scientific notation, in which a number is treated as a fraction (between 0.1 and 1.0), times a power of 10. The *magnitude* (sign not considered) of the number so represented must lie between the approximate limits of 10^{-38} and 10^{+38} or be zero.*

We see that a fixed point number is always an integer, whereas a floating point number may be an integer or have a fractional part. Furthermore, FORTRAN carries out computations with floating point numbers in such a way that we do not have to be concerned with the location of decimal points. All questions of lining up decimal points before addition and subtraction, etc., are automatically taken care of by the computer. This is the reason for the term "floating point."

---

* These rather odd limits are based on the representation of numbers within the IBM 709, which uses *binary* numbers, i.e., numbers using only ones and zeros. We, however, are not required to study binary numbers, since FORTRAN handles all conversions between binary and decimal. Not all computers using FORTRAN are binary, of course, and not all binary computers represent numbers the way the 709 does. The limits on numbers for each FORTRAN system are given in Appendix 1.

A floating point number is always a rational real number. Irrational numbers and complex numbers are not permitted, although complex numbers can be handled by performing arithmetic on their real and imaginary parts separately.

Any number that appears in literal explicit form in a statement is called a *constant*, whereas a quantity that is given a name is called a *variable*. For instance, we shall see a little later that the following are arithmetic statements:

$$I = 2$$

$$X = A + 12.7$$

Here 2 and 12.7 are constants, I, X, and A are variables.

FORTRAN distinguishes between floating and fixed-point constants by the presence or absence of a decimal point, respectively. Thus 3 is a fixed point constant, but 3.0 (3., 3.000, etc.) is a floating point. The two forms are *not* interchangeable because they are stored and processed within the computer in entirely different ways.

If a constant is positive, it may be preceded by a plus sign or not, as desired. If it is negative, it must be preceded by a minus sign.

The following are acceptable fixed point constants:

$$0$$
$$6$$
$$+400$$
$$-1234$$
$$32767$$

The following are *not* acceptable fixed point constants:

12.78   (decimal point not allowed)
123456 (too large*)

The following are acceptable floating point constants:

$$0.0$$
$$6.0$$
$$6.$$
$$-20000.$$
$$-.0002784$$
$$+15.016$$

We see that the characteristic decimal point may appear at the beginning of the number, at the end, or between two digits. A floating point constant may have any number of digits, but only a little

more than eight digits of significance will be retained by the computer. In other words, although there is no restriction on the number of digits in a floating point constant, it makes sense to use only eight or nine at most.

It is possible to follow a floating point constant by the letter E and a one- or two-digit positive or negative power of ten by which the number is to be multiplied. This simplifies the writing of very large or very small numbers. Thus the following are all further examples of acceptable floating point constants:

TABLE 1.1

Constant	Equivalent to
5.0E + 6	$5.0 \cdot 10^6$
−7.E − 12	$-7.0 \cdot 10^{-12}$
6.205E12	$6.205 \cdot 10^{12}$
−.1E7	$-0.1 \cdot 10^7$

1.4   Variables and the Names of Variables

The term *variable* is used in FORTRAN to denote any quantity that is referred to by name rather than by explicit appearance and which is able to take on a number of values instead of being restricted to one value.

Variables may be either fixed point or floating point quantities. A fixed point variable is simply one that takes on any of the values permitted of a fixed point constant, namely, zero or any positive or negative integer no greater than 32767. The *name* of a fixed point variable is one to six digits or letters, of which the first is I, J, K, L, M, or N. Examples of acceptable names of fixed point variables: I, KLM, MATRIX, L123, I6M2K. Examples of unacceptable names of fixed point variables: J123456 (too many characters), ABC (does not begin with the correct letter), 5M (does not begin with a letter), $J78 (contains a character other than a digit or a letter), J34.5 (contains a character other than a digit or a letter).

A floating point variable is one represented inside the machine in the same form as a floating point constant. Generally, most data will be set up as floating point variables because of the convenience provided by the automatic handling of all decimal points. The name of a floating point variable is one to six digits or letters, of which the first is a letter but *not* I, J, K, L, M, or N. Examples of acceptable names of floating point variables: AVAR, R51TX, FRONT, G, F0009, SVECT. Examples of unacceptable names of floating point variables: A123456 (too many characters), 8BOX (does not begin with a letter), KJL1 (does not begin with the correct letter), *BCD (contains a character other than a digit or a letter), A + B (contains a character other than a digit or a letter), B9.35 (contains a character other than a digit or a letter).

With two exceptions, noted below, the assignment of names to the variables appearing in a program is entirely under the control of the programmer. Care must be taken to observe the rule for distinguishing between the names of fixed and floating point variables, but one learns fairly readily to avoid this pitfall. If this rule is violated, FORTRAN will in some cases reject the program and in other cases give results that are not what the programmer intended. It should be noted that the compiler places no significance on names; it merely inspects the first letter to determine whether the variable is fixed or floating point. A name such as B7 specifically *does not* mean B times 7, B to the seventh power, or B_7. If the programmer chooses to assign names that simplify recall of the meaning of the variable, this is perfectly acceptable, but no such meaning is attached to the symbols by the compiler. It should also be noted that every combination of letters and digits constitutes a separate name. Thus the name ABC is not the same as the name BAC, and the names A, AB, and AB7 are all distinct.

There are two restrictions on the free invention of variable names (in addition to the restriction on the first character). We shall see that it is possible to have *subscripted* variables. The first rule states that the name of a subscripted variable must not end in F. A safe policy is *never* to use a variable name ending in F. We shall also see that FORTRAN provides a number of *functions* for evaluating commonly used mathematical functions and for other purposes. Every function has been assigned a name; for instance, the name of the function that takes a square root is SQRTF. The names of all functions end in F. The second rule states that no variable may have a name that is the same as the name of a function or that is the same as the name of a function without its final F. Thus SQRTF and SQRT are both prohibited as the names of variables.

1.5 Operations and Expressions

FORTRAN provides for five basic operations: addition, subtraction, multiplication, division, and exponentiation. Each of these operations is represented by a distinct symbol:

Addition	+
Subtraction	−
Multiplication	*
Division	/
Exponentiation	**

Note that the combination ** is considered to be one symbol; there is no confusion between ** and *, since, as we shall see, it is never permissible to write two operation symbols side by side. These are the only operations allowed; any other mathematical operations must either be built up from the basic five or computed by using the functions discussed later.

The term *expression* is used in its precise mathematical sense in FORTRAN. An expression is defined as a constant, variable, or function, or any combination of these separated by operation symbols, commas, and parentheses, which forms a meaningful mathematical expression. Some examples of expressions and their meanings are shown in Table 1.2.

In writing expressions, the programmer must observe certain rules in order to convey his intentions correctly.

1. Two operation symbols must not appear next to each other. Thus A*−B is not a valid expression but A*(−B) is.

2. Parentheses must be used to indicate groupings just as in ordinary mathematical notation. Thus $(X + Y)^3$ must be written (X + Y)**3 to convey the correct meaning. Again, A − B + C and A − (B + C) are both legitimate expressions, but they do not mean the same thing.

3. The ambiguous expression A^{B^C} must be written as A**(B**C) or as (A**B)**C, whichever is intended. It should not be written as A**B**C.

4. When the hierarchy of operations in an expression is not completely specified by the use of parentheses, the sequence is all exponentiations are performed first, then all multiplications and divisions, and finally all additions and subtractions.

TABLE 1.2

Expression	Meaning
K	The value of the fixed point variable K
3.14159	The value of the floating point constant 3.14159
A + 2.1828	The sum of the value of A and 2.1828
RHO − SIGMA	The difference of the values of RHO and SIGMA
X*Y	The product of the values of X and Y
OMEGA/6.2832	The quotient of the value of OMEGA and 6.2832
C**2	The value of C raised to the second power
(A + F)/(X + 2.)	The sum of the values of A and F divided by the sum of the value of X and 2
1./(X**2 + Y**3)	The reciprocal of $(X^2 + Y^3)$

Thus the following two expressions are equivalent:

a. A*B + C/D − E**F
b. (A*B) + (C/D) − (E**F).

As another example, X*Y**3 means $X \cdot Y^3$, not $(X \cdot Y)^3$. Note that this rule applies *only* in the absence of parentheses. Thus the expression (X*Y)**3 means $(X \cdot Y)^3$, since Rule 2 takes precedence.

5. Within a sequence of consecutive multiplications and/or divisions, or additions and/or subtractions, in which the order of the operations to be performed is not completely specified by the use of parentheses, the operations are performed from left to right. Thus the expression

A/B*C would be taken to mean $\frac{A}{B} \cdot C$, not $\frac{A}{B \cdot C}$, and I − J + K would mean (I − J) + K, not I − (J + K). With respect to addition and sub-

traction, this rule applies only to certain uncommon situations in which large or small numbers occur. For all practical purposes it may be considered simply to define what FORTRAN will do with expressions that in ordinary mathematical notation are considered ambiguous, such as A/B·C.

6. Although any expression may be raised to a power that is a positive or negative fixed point quantity, only floating point expressions may be raised to a floating point power. An exponent may itself be any expression. Thus the expression X**(I + 2) is perfectly acceptable.

7. Fixed and floating point quantities must not be "mixed" in the same expression; however, fixed point quantities may appear in floating point expressions as exponents and as subscripts (see Chapter 5). There are exceptions also in the use of some functions, although not with any in this text (see Chapter 2).

TABLE 1.3

Mathematical Notation	Correct Expression	Incorrect Expression
$A \cdot B$	A*B	AB (No operation)
$A \cdot (-B)$	A*(−B) or −A*B	A*−B (two operations side by side)
$A + 2$	A + 2.	A + 2 (mixed fixed and floating point)
$-(A + B)$	−(A + B)	−A + B or − + A + B
A^{I+2}	A**(I + 2)	A**I + 2(= A^I + 2, mixed)
$A^{B+2} \cdot C$	A**(B + 2.)*C	A**B + 2.*C(= A^B + 2·C)
$\frac{A \cdot B}{C \cdot D}$	A*B/(C*D) or A/C*B/D	A*B/C*D $\left(= \frac{ABD}{C}\right)$
$\left(\frac{A + B}{C}\right)^{2.5}$	((A + B)/C)**2.5	(A + B)/C**2.5 $\left(= \frac{A + B}{C^{2.5}}\right)$
A[X + B(X + C)]	A*(X + B*(X + C))	A(X + B(X + C))

8. Parentheses indicate grouping (with the exception of their application to subscripted variables and functions). Specifically, they never imply multiplication. Thus, the expression $(A + B)(C + D)$ is incorrect; it should be written $(A + B)*(C + D)$.

Table 1.3 shows some examples of correct and incorrect ways of forming FORTRAN expressions.

EXERCISES

1. Write the following numbers as FORTRAN floating point constants:

16, 4.59016, $-10{,}000$, 10^{17}, 0.0000000006, -1, -10^{-10}

*2. All of the following are unacceptable floating point constants. Why?

12,345.0,   +234,   1.6E63,   1E -7

*3. Do the following pairs of floating point constants represent the same number in each case?

a. 16.9   +16.9
b. 23000.   2.3E4
c. 0.000007   .7E -5
d. 1.0   1.
e. .906E5   +906.0E $+2$

4. Which of the following are acceptable names of fixed point variables, which are acceptable names of floating point variables, and which are unacceptable names? Do all acceptable names represent different variables?

X, I12G, CAT, X $+2$, XP2, NEXT, 42G, LAST,

XSQUARED, DELTA, MU, A*B, X1.4, (X61),

GAMMA81, AI, IA, X12, 1X2, GAMMA, KAPPA

5. Write FORTRAN expressions corresponding to each of the following mathematical expressions:

*a. $X + Y^3$ b. $(X + Y)^3$

c. X^4 *d. $A + \dfrac{B}{C}$

e. $\dfrac{A + B}{C}$ *f. $A + \dfrac{B}{C + D}$

g. $\dfrac{A + B}{C + D}$ *h. $\left(\dfrac{A + B}{C + D}\right)^2 + X^2$

i. $\dfrac{A + B}{C + \dfrac{D}{F + G}}$ *j. $1 + X + \dfrac{X^2}{2!} + \dfrac{X^3}{3!}$

*k. $\left(\dfrac{X}{Y}\right)^{G-1}$ l. $\dfrac{\dfrac{A}{B} - 1}{G\left(\dfrac{G}{D} - 1\right)}$

6. Shown below are a number of mathematical expressions and corresponding FORTRAN expressions. All contain at least one error. Point out the errors and write correct expressions.

a. $(X + Y)^4$ X + Y**4

*b. $\dfrac{X + 2}{Y + 4}$ X + 2.0/Y + 4.0

c. $\dfrac{A \cdot B}{C + 2}$ AB/(C + 2.)

d. $-\dfrac{(-X + Y - 16)}{Y^3}$ $-(-X + Y - 16)/$ Y**3

*e. $\left(\dfrac{X + A + \pi}{2Z}\right)^2$ (X + A + 3.1416)/ (2.0*Z)**2

f. $\left(\dfrac{X}{Y}\right)^{N-1}$ (X/Y)**N -1

*g. $\left(\dfrac{X}{Y}\right)^{R-1}$ (X/Y)**(R -1)

h. $\dfrac{A}{B} + \dfrac{C \cdot D}{F \cdot G \cdot H}$ A/B + CD/FGH

i. $(A + B)(C + D)$ A + B*C + D

j. $A + BX + CX^2 + DX^3$ $= A + X[B + X(C + DX)]$ A + X(B + X* (C + D*X)

k. $\dfrac{1{,}600{,}042X + 10^5}{4{,}309{,}992X + 10^5}$ (1,600,042X + 1E5)/ (4,309,992X + 1E5)

l. $\dfrac{1}{A^2}\left(\dfrac{R}{10}\right)^A$ 1/A**2*(R/10)**A

7. The following expressions are all acceptable, but each contains at least one pair of parentheses which can be removed without changing the meaning of the expression. Rewrite the expressions with the minimum number of parentheses.

a. (A*B)/C
b. (A/B)*C
c. (A + X)(B/Y)
d. (A**(I + 2) + B**(I + 3) + (X + 2.)*(B))
e. (A**(I $-$ J + 1))/(A**(I $-$ J + 1) + 6.28)
f. (((A) + (B)) + (C)(D)**2)/(((A + 2.8)** (I $-$ 1) + B/(C + D))*(A + 6.))
g. ((((((A/B)*C)/D)*R) + (A/(S**K)) $-$ (((B**2)*T)/(W**4)))

Answers to starred exercises are given at the back of the book, following Appendix 2.

2. ARITHMETIC STATEMENTS, FUNCTIONS

2.1 Writing and Punching a Program

A FORTRAN program, as we have noted, is made up of a series of *statements*, each of which is either an order to carry out some operation or a source of information to the compiler about the program. The program is written on a form similar to the one shown in Figure 2.1, with one or more lines for each statement. The information on each line is then punched into a card similar to the one shown in Figure 2.2. As outlined, this deck of cards is then read into the computer under control of the FORTRAN program and compiled into a set of machine instructions that will carry out the procedure specified by the statements.

In order to be able to show sample programs written on a standard form, it is necessary to describe briefly the purpose of each part of the form.

The numbers shown above the first line of the coding form stand for the card columns into which the information on the form will be punched. The first *field* (group of columns) on the form, columns 1 to 5, contains the *statement number*, if any. The use of statement numbers is described in Chapter 4.

Column 1 has another function, that of indicating a *comment card*. If column 1 contains a "C," then FORTRAN does not expect to find a statement on the card and, in fact, does not process the information on the card. Although the comment cards are not processed by FORTRAN, they will appear on any listing of the program deck and/or on a listing produced as a by-product of the compilation process. Comment cards may be used freely to give information about the program to anyone who may have to read it. Liberal use of comments can be valuable to the original programmer, as well, if the program has to be modified after a long period of not looking at it. FORTRAN programs are a great deal easier to read than programs written in actual machine instructions, but it can still be difficult to understand the purpose of a complex program if there are no comments.

Column 6 is used to indicate a *continuation card*. If the statement can be punched entirely on one card, column 6 may be left blank or punched with a zero. If more than one card is required for a statement, the cards after the first (up to a maximum of nine) must be punched with some nonzero character. The first card of a continued statement must still have a zero or a blank in column 6. It is recommended that a zero be punched in column 6 of the first card of a continued statement and that the continuation cards be numbered consecutively, starting with 1.

The statement itself is punched in columns 7 to 72. *Blanks in this field are ignored by FORTRAN.* Blanks may thus be freely used to improve readability. The statement need not begin in column 7; some programmers, for instance, indent the continua-

C FOR COMMENT STATEMENT NUMBER	Cont.	FORTRAN STATEMENT	
1 5	6	7	72
27		READ 612, Q, R, C, AL	
612		FØRMAT (4F10.0)	
		IF(R**2 - 4.*AL/C) 10, 12, 12	
10		F0 = 0.1592*SQRTF(1./(AL*C))	
		F1 = 0.1592*SQRTF(1./(AL*C) - R**2/(4.*AL**2))	
		DELT = 0.1/F0	
		AIM = 6.2832*F0**2*Q/F1	
		C1 = R/(2.*AL)	
		C2 = 6.2832*F1	
		T = 0.	
		DØ 11 J = 1, 100	
		AI = AIM * EXPF(-C1*T) * SINF(C2*T)	
		PRINT 706, T, AI	
706		FØRMAT(2E20.8)	
11		T = T + DELT	
		GØ TØ 27	
12		STØP	
		END	

Figure 2.1.   An example of a FORTRAN source program.

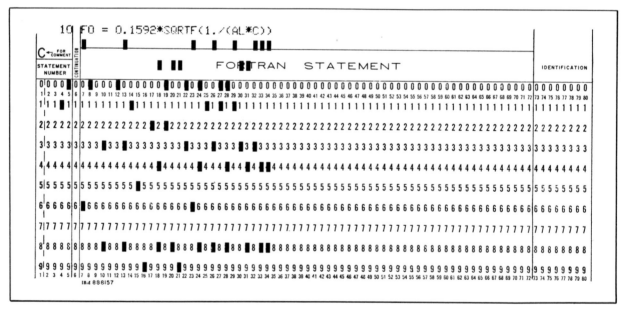

Figure 2.2.   An example of a FORTRAN statement card.   Compare line 10 of Figure 2.1 with this card and note that the characters punched in the columns are printed at the top.

tions of a long statement to make it a little clearer that continuation is involved. Some programmers like to leave a space on both sides of each operation symbol for readability. All such conventions are at the discretion of the programmer.

Nevertheless, it is necessary to indicate clearly exactly how many spaces are desired at each point, to allow for verification of the punching of the cards. It is for this reason that most FORTRAN coding forms have a box for each character or at least a short vertical line to indicate the character divisions.

Columns 73 to 80 are not processed by FORTRAN and may be used for any desired card or program identification.

It is essential that the coding forms be filled out with great care and attention to detail. The statements must always be written in exactly the format specified; if a comma is misplaced or omitted the program will not be compiled or it will be compiled incorrectly. It is strongly recommended that only capital letters be used and that great care be taken to write certain easily confused characters in a distinctive manner. Various conventions are available for distinguishing between such characters as "oh" and "zero." One acceptable way to write

The digit one: 1	The letter I: I
The digit zero: 0	The letter O: $\emptyset$
The digit two: 2	The letter Z: $\not{Z}$
The digit five: 5	The letter S: S

Figure 2.3

these characters is shown in Figure 2.3. Greek letters are, of course, not permitted.

2.2 Arithmetic Statements

The most common statement is the *arithmetic statement*, which is an order to FORTRAN to perform a computation. Its general format is $a = b$, in which a is a variable name, written without a sign, and b is any expression defined above. The equal sign in an arithmetic statement is not used in the same way it is in ordinary mathematical notation. We are not allowed to write statements such as Z − RHO = ALPHA + BETA, in which Z is unknown and the others are known. The only legitimate form of arithmetic statement is one in which the left side of the statement is the name of a single variable. The precise meaning of the equal sign is then: *replace the value of the variable named on the left with the value of the expression on the right.* Thus the statement A = B + C is an order to form the sum of the values of the variables B and C and to replace the value of the variable A with that sum. The previous value of the variable A is lost. The statement GAMMA = 1.67 is an order to replace the value of the variable GAMMA with 1.67.

Another example of arithmetic statement brings out very forcefully the special meaning of the equal sign. A statement such as N = N + 1 has the meaning: *replace the value of the variable N*

TABLE 2.1

Arithmetic Statement	Original Formula
R = (A + B*X)/(C + D*X)	$R = \dfrac{A + BX}{C + DX}$
BETA = −1./(2.*X) + A**2/(4.*X**2)	$\beta = \dfrac{-1}{2X} + \dfrac{A^2}{4X^2}$
FY = X*(X**2 − Y**2)/(X**2 + Y**2)	$Fy = X \cdot \dfrac{X^2 - Y^2}{X^2 + Y^2}$
C = 1.112*D*R1*R2/(R1 − R2)	$C = 1.112D \dfrac{r_1 r_2}{r_1 - r_2}$
Y = (1.E − 6 + A*X**3)**(2./3.)	$Y - (10^{-6} + AX^3)^{2/3}$
J = 4*K − 6*K1*K2	$J = 4K - 6k_1 k_2$
I = I + 1	
K = 12	K = 12
PI = 3.1415927	$\pi = 3.1415927$
M = 2*M + 10*J	$M_{new} = 2M_{old} + 10J$

TABLE 2.2

Incorrect Statement	Error
Y = 2.X + A	*missing
3.14 = X − A	Left side must be a variable name
A = ((X + Y)A**2 + (R − S)**2/16.7	Not the same number of left and right parentheses; *missing
X = 1,624,009.*DELTA	Commas not allowed in constants
−J = I**2.	Fixed point quantities may not be raised to floating point powers; variable on left must not be written with a sign
BX6 = 1./ − 2.*A**6	Two operation symbols side-by-side not permitted, even though the minus is not intended as indicating subtraction
DERIV = N*X**(N − 1)	"Mixing" fixed and floating point this way not permitted

with its old value plus 1. This sort of statement, which is clearly not an equation, finds frequent use.

It is never correct to have fixed and floating point quantities mixed in any way except in fixed point exponents of floating point expressions, fixed point subscripts of floating point variables (Chapter 4), and certain functions. A computation such as 2*X will always give an incorrect result, since we are mixing the fixed point constant 2 with the floating point variable X. In most such cases FORTRAN will not compile the statement; if it is accepted, the result will be doubtful.

The examples in Table 2.1 show acceptable arithmetic statements with their equivalent normal mathematical forms when such equivalents exist. Variable names have been chosen arbitrarily; any other legitimate names would be just as good. We are also assuming, of course, that previous statements have established values of the variables on the right-hand sides.

The examples in Table 2.2 are presented to emphasize once again the importance of writing expressions and statements in the prescribed format. All of the examples in Table 2.2 contain at least one error.

2.3   FORTRAN Arithmetic

Most arithmetic operations on data should be programmed as floating point operations in order to avoid decimal-point location problems and to work conveniently with fractions. However, cases will arise occasionally in which it is necessary to do fixed point arithmetic. Since pitfalls await the unwary, it is necessary to describe precisely how fixed point arithmetic is done.

The fundamental consideration is that if a fixed point computation gives a result that is not an integer the result is *truncated* to a whole number rather than rounded; that is, any fractional part is simply discarded. For instance, the result of the fixed point division 5/3 is 1, not 2. This applies only to division; additions, subtractions, and multiplications on fixed point quantities give correct integral results.

Expressions that involve sequences of operations including divisions require caution in the grouping of the operations. This is the one occasion in which Rule 5 on p. 7 is of practical importance. For instance, if we carry out the calculation 5/3*6, the result will be 6, not 10 or 12. The rule states that in a sequence of multiplications and divisions in which no parentheses appear the calculations are performed from left to right. Thus 5 would be divided by 3 and the result truncated to 1, which would be multiplied by 6 to give the result of 6. On the other hand, if the expression is written as 5*6/3, 6*5/3, 5*(6/3), or (6/3)*5, the result will be 10. This somewhat bothersome fact is ordinarily only an academic consideration because most programs will be set up with floating point arithmetic, in which the problem does not arise. In floating point all fractional results are retained to as much significance as space within the number allows. The calculation in the example would give a floating point 10, however the expression is written (but note next paragraph).

Even with floating point arithmetic, there is a precaution to be observed. Because of rounding errors and the fact that most fractions have only approximate decimal representations, results that should be integers may not come out as integers. For instance, suppose we were to perform the calculation 1./3.*3., which, we recall, means (1./3.)*3. The result clearly should be 1.0000000, but it will not be. The result of the division, to eight decimal places, is 0.33333333. When this is multiplied by 3, we get 0.99999999, not 1.0000000. The unsuspecting programmer may be understandably surprised by such a result. This annoyance is no fault of FORTRAN; it is unavoidable in the use of any digital computer. One must simply be aware that such things can happen and take appropriate steps to handle properly any situation in which problems could arise. It happens fairly often that provisions must be made for such things in programming, and one must be prepared for strange-appearing results.

In most cases the variables in an arithmetic statement will be either all fixed point or all floating point, with a few exceptions as noted. However, it is permissible to have a fixed point variable on the left of an arithmetic statement with a floating point expression on the right and vice versa. If the variable on the left is fixed point and the expression on the right is floating point, then the entire computation will be done in floating point and the final result truncated to an integer before being stored as the new value of the variable on the left. If the variable on the left is floating point and the expression is fixed point, then the entire computation will be done in fixed point, with truncation of any nonintegral results after each operation, and the final result converted to floating point form. These situations will have occasional usefulness.

A final word of caution. Although the allowable range of number sizes will be entirely adequate for most problems, there is the possibility that a result will exceed the limits. To review, these limits are: fixed point quantities must not exceed 32767, and floating point quantities must either be zero or lie between 10^{-38} and 10^{+38} in absolute value (sign not considered). If the result of a computation exceeds these limits, an indication will be given in some cases; the nature of the indication, if any, depends on the version of FORTRAN being used.

2.4 Mathematical Functions

FORTRAN provides for the use of certain common mathematical functions, such as square root, logarithm, exponential, sine, cosine, arctangent, and absolute value. The exact list of functions available depends on the version of FORTRAN being used and to a certain extent on the particular computer installation. Every FORTRAN system, however, makes provision for computing the functions named above.

Every function has a preassigned name. The name for the square root function is SQRTF; the name for the exponential function is EXPF. These names in general vary with the different versions of FORTRAN, but those of the elementary mathematical functions are fairly standard. The functions that we shall use and their names are as follows:

TABLE 2.3

Mathematical Function	FORTRAN Name
Square Root	SQRTF
Exponential	EXPF
Sine of an angle in radians	SINF
Cosine of an angle in radians	COSF
Arctangent; angle given in radians	ATANF
Natural logarithm	LOGF
Absolute Value	ABSF

In order to make use of a mathematical function, it is necessary only to write the name of the function and to follow it with an expression enclosed in parentheses. This directs FORTRAN to compute the named function of the value represented by the expression in parentheses.

As an example of the use of functions, suppose it is necessary to compute the cosine of an angle named X. This angle must be expressed in radians. Writing COSF(X) in a statement will result in the computation of the cosine of the angle. In this example the *argument* of the function is the single variable X. This is by no means a necessity; the argument may be *any* expression, with the one restriction that in all of the mathematical functions mentioned above the argument must be a floating point quantity and the function value is computed in floating point form. If, for example, we wanted the square root of $B^2 - 4AC$, we would simply write SQRTF(B**2 − 4.*A*C).

A function may be written in a statement wherever the function value is desired. If, for instance, we are using the square root function in computing one of the two roots of a quadratic equation, we could write a statement

ROOT1

$$= (-B + SQRTF(B**2 - 4.*A*C))/(2.*A)$$

It may be well to review the purpose of the parentheses here. Those enclosing B**2 − 4.*A*C are required to enclose the argument of the square root function. The parentheses around the numerator in the formula indicate that everything before the slash is to be divided by what follows. The parentheses enclosing the 2.*A indicate that the A is in the denominator; without this final set, the result would be to divide the numerator by 2 and then multiply the entire fraction by A.

For another example suppose that we are required to evaluate the formula

$$\text{HENRY} = 2 \cdot 10^{-9} X \left(\log \frac{2X}{D} - 1 + \frac{D}{X} \right)$$

which gives the mutual inductance between two wires of length X separated by a distance D. The inductance may be computed by writing the following statement:

HENRY = 2.E−9*X*

$$(LOGF(2.*X/D) - 1.0 + D/X)$$

It is perfectly permissible for the argument of one function to involve another function. This is illustrated by a statement we may write out to carry out the following computation, which arises in the calculation of a certain integral:

$$\text{VAL} = \frac{1}{\cos X} + \log \left| \tan \frac{X}{2} \right|$$

Since we have no function for taking the tangent of an angle, we will compute the tangent from the formula:

$$\tan \theta = \frac{\sin \theta}{\cos \theta}$$

The statement to compute this value could be as follows:

VAL = 1./COSF(X)

$$+ LOGF(ABSF(SINF(X/2.)/COSF(X/2.)))$$

That part of the statement following the plus sign calls for the computation of the logarithm of the absolute value of the sine over the cosine. All of the parentheses here are essential; in each case they simply enclose the argument of a function.

This statement gives the same result as the following set of statements, where the statements would be executed in sequence.

$$Y = X/2.$$

$$TAN = SINF(Y)/COSF(Y)$$

$$AB = ABSF(TAN)$$

$$VAL = 1./COSF(X) + LOGF(AB)$$

Now, each function has an argument consisting of only one variable. In one version of FORTRAN it is required that functions be used in this manner. In the others it may always be done if desired to reduce the complexity of a statement. In fact, such simplifying substitutions are often a good idea even in computations not involving functions, just to keep the statements simple and easy to work with.

EXERCISES

1. Each of the arithmetic statements below contains at least one error. Identify them.

a. +V = A + B   b. V − 3.96 = X**1.67
c. 4 = I   d. X = (A + 6)**2
e. ((A + BZ6)*(A**3 + Y*X2))*X/3.
f. K6 = I**A

2. State the value of A or I stored as the result of each of the following arithmetic statements and whether the result is in fixed or floating point form.

*a. A = 2*6 + 1   j. A = 6.0*(1.0/6.0)
*b. A = 2/3   *k. A = 1./3. + 1./3. + 1./3.
c. A = 2.*6./4.   l. A = (4.0)**(3/2)
d. I = 2*10/4   m. A = (4.0)**3./2.
e. I = 2(10/4)   *n. A = (4.0)**(3./2.)
f. A = 2(10/4)   *o. I = 19/4 + 5/4
g. A = 2.*(10./4.)   p. A = 19/4 + 5/4
h. A = 2.0*(1.0E1/4.0)   q. I = 100*(99/100)
i. A = 6.0*1.0/6.0

3. Write arithmetic statements to compute the following formulas, using FORTRAN coding paper if possible. Use the letters in the formulas for variable names.

*a. $\text{AREA} = 2 \cdot P \cdot R \cdot \sin(\pi/P)$

b. $\text{CHORD} = 2R \sin \dfrac{A}{2}$

*c. $\text{ARC} = 2\sqrt{Y^2 + (4X^2/3)}$

d. $S = -\dfrac{\cos^4 X}{4}$

*e. $S = -\dfrac{\cos^{P+1} X}{P+1}$

f. $R = \dfrac{\sin^3 X \cos^2 X}{5} + \dfrac{2}{15} \sin^3 X$

*g. $G = \dfrac{1}{2} \log \dfrac{1 + \sin X}{1 - \sin X}$

h. $D = \log |\sec X + \tan X|$

*i. $E = X \arctan \dfrac{X}{A} - \dfrac{A}{2} \log (A^2 + X^2)$

j. $F = -\dfrac{\pi}{2} \log|X| + \dfrac{A}{X} - \dfrac{A^3}{3^2 X^3}$

k. $Z = -\dfrac{1}{\sqrt{X^2 - A^2}} - \dfrac{2A^2}{3(\sqrt{X^2 - A^2})^3}$

*l. $Q = \left(\dfrac{2}{\pi X}\right)^{\frac{1}{2}} \sin X$

m. $B = \dfrac{e^{X/\sqrt{2}} \cos (\sqrt{X/2} + \pi/8)}{\sqrt{2\pi X}}$

*n. $Y = (2\pi)^{\frac{1}{2}} X^{X+1} e^{-X}$

o. $T = A \cdot e^{-\sqrt{W/2P} \cdot X}$

3. INPUT AND OUTPUT STATEMENTS

3.1 The READ and FORMAT Statements

If a problem is to be done only once, the data can be entered with the program in the form of constants in statements. This is ordinarily not the case, however; programs are usually set up to read in the data from cards at the time the program is executed. The same program can then be used to solve the same problem with as many sets of data as desired.

Data is entered into the computer by the execution of a READ statement that lists the names of the variables for which new values are to be read from a card. The new values must be punched on the card in the same sequence as the variable names are listed in the READ statement. Thus there is a sort of scanning process: the first value on the card goes with the first variable name, the second value with the second variable name, etc., for as many variable names and data values as there are. This scanning goes from left to right and begins with the first (leftmost) data value on the card. Furthermore, the execution of a READ statement *always* initiates the reading of a new card. If, for instance, there are six data values punched on one card, they cannot be entered with two READ statements, the second picking up where the first left off. The only way to enter the six numbers from one card is to provide a READ statement that lists the names of all six variables.

So far we have discussed how to provide three items of information about the input operation:

1. What data medium is to be used and whether this is an input or output operation: the word READ clearly implies input and at the same time specifies reading a *card*.

2. Which variables in the program are to receive new values: this is specified by listing their names in the READ statement.

3. The order in which the values appear on the card: this is specified by the order in which their names appear in the READ statement.

There is one more item of information required: in what format are the data values punched on the card? * How many columns are allocated to each value? Is the value fixed or floating point, and, if floating, is there an exponent? If the value does not contain an explicit decimal point, where should the decimal point be assumed to be?

This information is provided by a FORMAT statement. A complete discussion of this rather extensive subject would be out of place here and is deferred to Chapter 7. We may, however, get the basic ideas by considering an example. Suppose that it is desired to read new values of three variables named A, I, and X. The values are punched on a card as shown in Figure 3.1. Such a card could be read by the two statements shown in Figure 3.2.

* This section does not apply to FORTRAN or GOTRAN for the IBM 1620, FORTRAN for the IBM 1401, or any of the versions of FORTRAN for the IBM 650. In these systems format is either fixed or specified in other ways. Users of these systems may skip this discussion of the FORMAT statement; they should consult the appropriate manual for information on data formats.

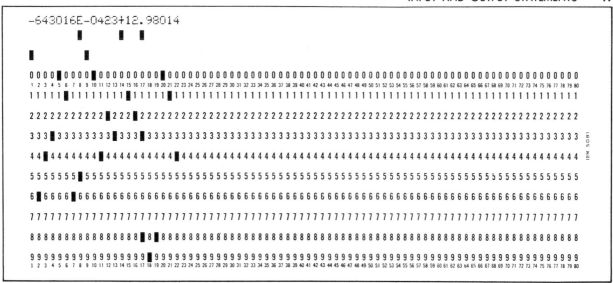

Figure 3.1. Data card for reading by the statements in Figure 3.2.

The 69 in front of the FORMAT statement is its *statement number;* this number was chosen arbitrarily. As we shall see in Chapter 4, statement numbers may be assigned freely in order to establish cross references within a program. Here we use a statement number to identify the FORMAT statement that is associated with the READ statement.

The scanning process mentioned earlier carries over to the FORMAT statement. The first *field specification,* the E11.5, is automatically associated with the first *field* (number, or group of columns) on the card; the second field specification, the I2, is associated with the second field; and the F9.0 is associated with the third field.

Looking now at the card, we see that the first field is made up of eleven columns, signified by the "11" in E11.5. The number is floating point, and it has an exponent (the E − 04), signified by the "E." The "5" in E11.5 means that the number from the card is to be treated as though there were five places to the right of the (as-

sumed) decimal point, that is, as though the number were $-6.43016E - 04$ ($= -6.43016 \cdot 10^{-4} = -0.000643016$). To summarize, E11.5 means that the new data value is punched in a field of eleven columns, that it is a floating point number with an exponent, and that there are five places to the right of the decimal point (which, to save work, is not actually punched).

The second field specification is easier, since it refers to a fixed point number, which requires less flexibility in format. The "I" indicates fixed point and the "2" means two columns. Notice on the card that the value is punched without a sign; if a value is positive, the plus sign is optional.

The third field introduces a new flexibility. The "F" indicates that the value is floating point but without an exponent. As we might expect, the "9" means nine columns and the "0" means no places after the decimal point. However, this convention on decimal points applies only if the decimal point is *not* punched. In this case there *is* a decimal point in the card value; the actual decimal

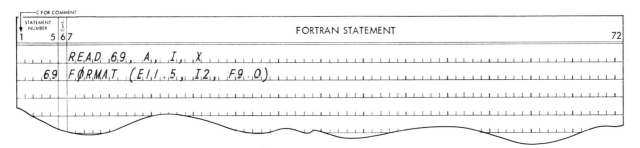

Figure 3.2. FORTRAN statements to read the data card shown in Figure 3.1.

point then takes precedence, and the number entered into the computer will be the floating point form of +12.98014, just as punched.

We have not by any means covered all of the flexibility provided by the FORMAT statement, but this much of an introduction should serve to indicate how the FORTRAN user is free to set up card formats as his needs and preferences dictate. We will note additional features of the FORMAT statement as we proceed; a more complete discussion appears in Chapter 7.

3.2 Summary of FORTRAN Compilation and Execution

To make effective use of a computer, using the FORTRAN system, it is vital to understand the relation between the source and object programs and how input and output operations tie in. We may summarize the procedure for getting a FORTRAN program in operation:

1. The program is written on coding sheets like the one shown in Figure 2.1. The program includes (ordinarily) READ and PRINT statements for reading data and printing results.

2. The program is punched onto cards. The result is the *source program deck*. It does *not* include data cards.

3. The FORTRAN compiler, which is a large program of machine instructions, is read into the computer from another deck of cards or from magnetic tape.

4. The FORTRAN compiler program reads the source program deck, *not* including any data cards, into the computer, compiles (translates) them into actual machine instructions, and punches the machine instructions onto another deck of cards called the *object program deck*. *The object program has not been executed and no data cards have been read.*

5. The FORTRAN compiler program is removed from the machine and the object program is read in. With the computer under control of the object program, the machine instructions produced from the READ statements in the source program can read the data cards and carry out the computation. The machine instructions produced from the PRINT statements cause the printing of results, and the machine instructions produced from any other input and output statements are executed.

It is extremely
clearly understood;
would be almost me
derstanding. This is
the short cuts that m
operation of programs.
of the machine instru
statements in the sourc
repeated as often as wou.
fore use such phrases as
ment is executed." It mu
this is an abbreviation fo
the actual execution occu.
pilation.

3.3 The PUNCH and PR

Problem results can be punch   ̶ ̶u a card by the PUNCH statement, which operates in a manner closely analogous to the READ statement. The names of the variables for which values are to be punched are listed after the FORMAT statement number, with commas separating variable names as before. The values appear on the card in the same order in which the variable names appear in the PUNCH statement; each value is punched in fixed or floating point, as the FORMAT statement dictates. A PUNCH statement always causes the punching of a card, with the first-named variable always being the first on the card. For each PUNCH statement another card is punched. There is no way to get several PUNCH statements to punch results on the same card.

In punching a card, the FORMAT statement is used to specify the arrangement of results on the card. The meanings of the field specifications are about the same, with due allowance for the fact that output is involved rather than input. "I" still indicates that a fixed point quantity is involved and that therefore it should be punched without a decimal point. "E" and "F" mean floating point; "E" means with an exponent and "F" means without. The digit following "I," "E," or "F" always specifies the number of columns allotted to the number, and with "E" and "F" the next digit specifies the number of places following the decimal point. A decimal point is always punched with "E" and "F."

A few examples may help to clarify these ideas. Suppose that the values of the three variables B, Y, and K are −410.46128, +12.614078, and +649,

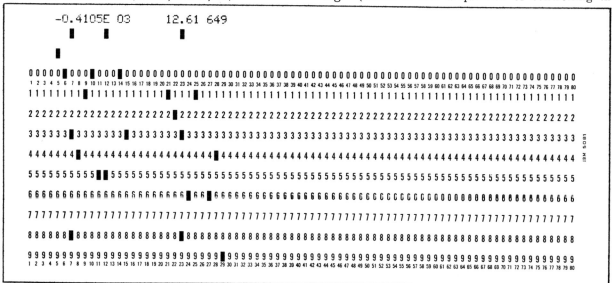

Figure 3.3. An example of a card produced by the PUNCH statement.

respectively. The following statements would result in punching the card of Figure 3.3:

PUNCH 40, B, Y, K

40 FORMAT (E15.8, F10.6, I4)

Note that plus signs are not punched.

Now suppose that we want to round off the first two numbers to four significant digits. This can be done by specifying fewer decimal places. The following two statements, with the same data values, would produce the card in Figure 3.4.

PUNCH 40, B, Y, K

40 FORMAT (E15.4, F10.2, I4)

Note that the numbers have been properly rounded and that they appear at the right of the assigned fields.

The PRINT statement presents no new concepts. It is completely analogous to the PUNCH statement, except, of course, that it results in the printing of one line of results instead of the punching of a card. On the IBM 709 and most other computers the line can contain as many as 120 *characters* (digits, letters, and other symbols). The operation of the FORMAT statement is exactly the same as with PUNCH. However, since ease of reading must be considered, it is usual to allow more columns for each number than when punching. (There is also a question of controlling the

Figure 3.4. An example of a card produced by the PUNCH statement.

spacing of the printer. This subject can be postponed to Chapter 7.)

The reader who wishes to write practice programs without spending excessive time on the formats of data and results may proceed as follows. For card input make all fields ten columns. For fixed point data (which is fairly uncommon) use a field specification of I10. For floating point data use a field specification of F10.0 and punch an actual decimal point in the field. Very seldom will data be too large or too small to fit in this field; when such an occasion arises, use some other field specification as required. For output the I10 field specification is still adequate for fixed point results. Floating point results, however, should be printed with an E20.8. The extra space improves readability; the "E" field specification will print the number with an exponent, avoiding any problems of the spacing of very large or small answers.

3.4   The PAUSE and STOP Statements

The PAUSE or STOP statement may be used whenever it is desired to stop executing statements in a program. There is normally a STOP at the end of the program, when the computation is finished, but there are other useful applications of the statements. A program is often set up to do a certain amount of checking on the input data, to make sure that it is consistent and that all data values are within reasonable limits for the problem being done. If anything is wrong, some indication must be given to the operator, which may be done with PAUSE or STOP. Occasionally a problem is set up so that the programmer may have the opportunity to inspect part of the output before continuing; this also requires the ability to stop the execution of the object program.

The two statements are very similar. Both stop the execution of the object program. Both take effect *only* when the object program is *executed*, that is, they do not cause the termination of the compilation. Both may be followed by a single unsigned fixed point octal number (a number written with the digits zero through seven), which will be displayed in the lights on the computer console when the statement is executed. This last is useful when there are numerous STOP or PAUSE statements and it is desired to inform the operator which of them caused the halt.

The difference between the two statements is

this: after a STOP statement the computer cannot conveniently be made to continue with the program, whereas the PAUSE statement allows the operator to press a button on the computer console and to resume execution of the program, beginning with the statement after the PAUSE.

There are major differences in local usage of the STOP and PAUSE statements. The users of large computing systems, in particular, try to avoid the wasted machine time caused by stopping if there is any other way out.

3.5   The END Statement

The END statement is used as a signal to the compiler that the end of the program has been reached. The last statement of every program *must* be an END, otherwise the program will not be compiled. The END statement is primarily intended to give information to the compiler about the program, and, in contrast to the PAUSE and STOP statements, it has an effect on the compilation. It marks the end of the source program and tells the compiler to complete the production of the object program.

3.6   An Illustrative Program

To illustrate how some of these statements may be used, consider the following simple problem. Suppose that we wish to evaluate the formula below for values of X, Y, and I that will be read in from a card:

$$R = 16.78 \cos 2\pi X + (Y + 1.667)^I$$

This is naturally a much smaller problem than would be practical to set up for FORTRAN solution, but it serves to illustrate the principles involved in using input and output statements. The complete program for reading in the data, carrying out the computation, and punching the result could be as shown in Figure 3.5.

The READ statement calls for the reading of values of X, Y, and I from a data card punched as in Figure 3.6, in which the values are taken to be -0.012, -4.53, and $+2$, respectively. The FORMAT statement follows the simplified method suggested at the end of Section 3.3. Note that a FORMAT statement may appear anywhere in a program; it is not required to follow the input or

STATEMENT NUMBER	Cont.	FORTRAN STATEMENT
1 5	6	7 72
		READ 10, X, Y, I
		R = 16.78 * CØSF(6.2832*X) + (Y + 1.667)**I
		PRINT 20, X,Y,I,R
		STØP
10		FØRMAT (2F10.0, I10)
20		FØRMAT (2E20.8, I10, E20.8)
		END

Figure 3.5. A FORTRAN program to evaluate the function described in the text.

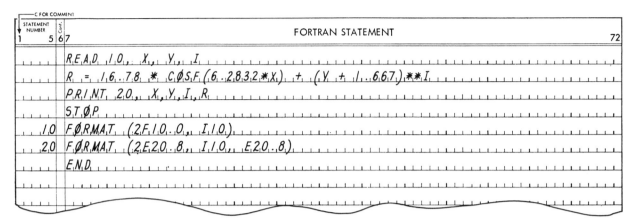

Figure 3.6. A data card for the program of Figure 3.5.

-0.12000000E-01   -0.45300000E 01   2   0.24929804E 02

Figure 3.7. A line printed by the program of Figure 3.5.

output statement that refers to it. Furthermore, there is no problem of the FORMAT statement "getting in the way" of other statements. It is never executed but merely provides information to the FORTRAN compiler; in common with the other *nonexecutable* statements that are considered later, it may appear anywhere in the source program. Notice finally that when the same field specification is used several times consecutively a *repetition number* may be written in front of it.

The PRINT statement prints the data values and the result. It is common practice to show the input data this way. Doing so makes it unnecessary to compare input and output listings to determine the answers corresponding to the data. The FORMAT statement is again the simplified type suggested earlier. Figure 3.7 shows the line that would be printed.

The STOP statement terminates the execution of the object program. In actual practice, this would be quite unusual; a common procedure would be to go back to the READ statement to repeat the whole program with new data. We consider how to do this in Chapter 4. The END statement simply signals to the FORTRAN compiler that the end of the source program has been reached.

EXERCISES

In each of the following exercises data values are to be read in, the values used in a computation, and results printed. The data values are to be printed along with the result for easy reference. In each exercise write a complete program, including STOP and END statements, on FORTRAN coding paper. Simplified FORMAT statements may be used. If a computer is available, programs may be compiled and run as a valuable exercise.

*1. READ: A, B, C
PRINT: A, B, C, S, AR
Evaluate:
$$S = \frac{(A + B + C)}{2}$$
$$AR = \sqrt{S(S - A)(S - B)(S - C)}$$

2. READ: A, B, C
PRINT: A, B, C, X1, X2
Evaluate:
$$X1 = \frac{-B + \sqrt{B^2 - 4AC}}{2A}$$
$$X2 = \frac{-B - \sqrt{B^2 - 4AC}}{2A}$$

3. READ: A, B, C, X
PRINT: A, B, C, X, R
Evaluate:
$$R = \frac{B \cdot C}{12}\left[6X^2\left(1 - \frac{X}{A}\right)^2 + B^2\left(1 - \frac{X}{A}\right)^4\right]$$

*4. READ: A, E, H, P
PRINT: A, E, H, P, X
Evaluate:
$$X = \frac{E \cdot H \cdot P}{(\sin A)\left(\dfrac{H^4}{16} + H^2P^2\right)}$$

5. READ: A, B, G1, G2, H1, H2
PUNCH: ATTR
Evaluate:
$$ATTR = \frac{H2 \cdot G1 \cdot G2}{A \cdot B}\tan^{-1}\frac{A \cdot B}{H1\sqrt{H1^2 + A^2 + B^2}}$$

*6. READ: A, X, S
PRINT: A, X, S, Y, Z
Evaluate:
$$Y = \sqrt{X^2 - A^2}$$
$$Z = \frac{X \cdot S}{2} - \frac{A^2}{2}\log|X + S|$$

7. READ: F, T, C, H, R
PUNCH: F, T, C, H, R, A, S
Evaluate:
$$A = \tan^{-1}\left(\frac{2\pi \cdot F \cdot H - \dfrac{1}{2\pi \cdot F \cdot C}}{R}\right)$$
$$S = \sin(2\pi \cdot F \cdot T - A)$$

4. TRANSFER OF CONTROL

4.1 Statement Numbers

In all of the examples presented so far it has been tacitly assumed that statements are executed sequentially. In many cases, however, we may wish to execute statements in some order other than the one-after-the-other sequence in which they are ordinarily taken. When this is desired, it is necessary to have some means by which a particular statement may be identified. This identification is provided by permitting each statement to have a *statement number*.

A statement number may be any positive number less than 32768; it is punched in columns 1 to 5 of the statement card.* No two statements may have the same number, but there is no requirement that every statement be numbered. Furthermore, there is no sequencing implied by the statement numbers. The first numbered statement need not bear the number 1, and statement numbers need not be assigned in an unbroken sequence or even in an ascending sequence. To emphasize this point: an acceptable sequence of statement numbers would be 500, 7, 9936, 9935, 9937, 200, and 259. Interspersed between the statements having these numbers could be statements having no statement numbers. In short, statement numbers provide a means of cross referencing when one statement must refer to another. They serve no other purpose.

---

* The allowable size of statement numbers varies in different versions of FORTRAN, as do the positions for punching them. The rules are summarized in Appendix 1, but it is best to see the appropriate manual for details.

4.2 The "GO TO" Statement

The GO TO statement provides a means of *transferring control* to some statement other than the next one in sequence. The statement takes the form GO TO n in which n is the number of another statement in the program. When such a statement is encountered, the next statement executed will be the one specified by the statement number. This statement is allowed to be any executable statement in the program, either before or after the GO TO statement itself.

A particularly simple usage of the GO TO statement is to return from the end of a program to its beginning, to execute it again. To illustrate this usage and also to provide another example of how FORTRAN may be applied, consider the following:

Suppose that we are required to compute the current flowing in an a-c circuit containing resistance, capacitance, and inductance. The current in such a circuit is given by

$$ I = \frac{E}{\sqrt{R^2 + \left(2\pi FL - \dfrac{1}{2\pi FC}\right)^2}} $$

where I = current, amperes
E = voltage, volts
R = resistance, ohms
L = inductance, henrys
C = capacitance, farads
F = frequency, cycles per second

We shall assume that the purpose of the computation is to provide the data for drawing a

```
┌── C FOR COMMENT
│ STATEMENT          │C│
│ NUMBER             │o│
│                    │n│
│ ▼                  │t│                                   FORTRAN STATEMENT
│ 1         5│6│7                                                                                        72
        READ 200, VØLT, ØHM, HENRY, FARAD
    200 FØRMAT (4F10.0)
     23 READ 200, CYCLE
        AMPER = VØLT/SQRTF(ØHM**2 + (6.2832*CYCLE*
      1 HENRY -1./(6.2832*CYCLE*FARAD))**2)
        PRINT 201, CYCLE, AMPER
    201 FØRMAT (2E20.8)
        GØ TØ 23
        END
```

Figure 4.1. A program to read data cards, compute a result, print the result, and return to read another data card. Note the continuation statement.

graph of the relation between current and frequency. Therefore, we shall regard the voltage, resistance, inductance, and capacitance as known and arrange to read in a series of values of frequency from cards and to print each given frequency, together with the computed value of current for each frequency. (We shall see later that if the desired values of the frequency are equally spaced or follow any other simple pattern the problem can be done without reading all the frequency values from cards.) After printing each answer, we shall simply return to the statement that reads a frequency card and start over.

In setting up the program, we immediately run into a minor difficulty. The symbols in the formula are not acceptable as variable names, since I and L would represent fixed point variables and we want all of the variables to be floating point. This is a problem that often arises; one must always be on guard to avoid inadvertently mixing fixed point and floating point computations. One solution to this problem is to prefix the unacceptable variable names with some letter that will make them floating point, which is perfectly satisfactory. However, we shall follow a different approach: the units in which the variables are expressed all happen to begin with the proper letters for floating point variables, and abbreviations for them may be used.

With this background, the program shown in Figure 4.1 is fairly straightforward. The first READ statement brings in the values of the four quantities in the formula that do not change. The second READ statement reads the first value of the frequency from another card. This has to be

made a separate statement because we want to be able to return to it without referring to the first READ statement; the four unchanging quantities need be read only once. Note that the arithmetic statement here has been written on two lines by use of a continuation card. The GO TO statement specifies that, after the frequency and the computed value of the current have been printed, control should return to the second READ statement, which has been given the statement number 23, to repeat the whole process. This will be done as long as there are further frequency cards to be read. When all the frequency cards have been read and the card hopper is empty, the machine will "hang up" on the reading operation, signifying the end of the computation. (This procedure cannot be recommended as a general practice; too much expensive machine time can be wasted. In general, some technique should be employed to signal the end of a computation in a more direct way, in keeping with the standard procedures of the particular computer installation. The procedure is shown here because it is *sometimes* acceptable on the smaller machines and because it simplifies this program— which is concerned with other things.)

4.3   The "IF" Statement

The GO TO statement provides a way to alter the sequence of statement execution *unconditionally*. Besides this, however, we need a way to change the sequence of statement execution *on the basis of what happens during execution of the pro-*

gram. In other words, we need a way of making a *conditional* transfer of control based on data or computed results. The IF statement provides this capability.

The IF statement is of the form

$$IF(e)\ n_1, n_2, n_3$$

where "e" stands for any expression and n_1, n_2, and n_3 are statement numbers. The operation of the statement is as follows: if the value of the expression within parentheses is negative, the statement having the statement number n_1 is executed next; if the value of expression is zero, statement n_2 is executed next; and if the expression is positive, statement n_3 is executed next.

For a simple example of the use of an IF statement consider a problem in definite integration. It is shown in calculus that the value of the integral, which we shall call Q, is governed entirely by whether the constant A is negative, zero, or positive:

$$Q = \int_0^\infty \frac{A\,dX}{A^2 + X^2} = \begin{cases} -\dfrac{\pi}{2} & \text{if } A < 0 \\ 0 & \text{if } A = 0 \\ +\dfrac{\pi}{2} & \text{if } A > 0 \end{cases}$$

Suppose we are doing a problem in which it is necessary to compute Q, assuming that A has already been determined by a previous computation. The program segment shown in Figure 4.2 will do this.

The IF statement here calls for an examination of the value of the variable A (we recall that a single variable—or for that matter a single constant—is included in the definition of an expres-

sion). If the value of the variable A is negative, statement 4 will be executed next, which calls for Q to be set equal to -1.5708, which is $-\pi/2$. After doing this we find the statement GO TO 3. If this statment were not there, the program would automatically go on in sequence to statement 5 where Q would be set equal to zero; this, of course, would not be what we desire. In other words, the GO TO 3 statement skips around the other parts of the program to statement 3, whatever it might be, where we presumably will make use of the value of Q that has been established. If the value of A is found to be zero, the IF statement causes a transfer to statement 5 where Q is set equal to zero and once again we skip around the rest of the program. If the value of A is found to be positive, the IF statement will cause a transfer of control to statement 6 where Q is set equal to $\pi/2$, and we then go on immediately to the next statement.

In another example of the use of the IF statement, suppose we are required to compute Y as a function of X by one of two different formulas:

$$Y = 0.5X + 0.95 \quad \text{if } X \leq 2.1$$
$$Y = 0.7X + 0.53 \quad \text{if } X > 2.1$$

This computation may be carried out by the program shown in Figure 4.3. The branch of the IF statement followed here depends on the value of the expression $X - 2.1$. If $X - 2.1$ is negative, X is obviously less than 2.1 and we transfer to statement 40, which computes Y according to the appropriate formula for that case. If X is equal to 2.1, we also get to the same formula, as required in the problem statement. If $X - 2.1$ is positive, then X is greater than 2.1 and we go to statement 30, which computes Y according to the appropriate

Figure 4.2. Program segment illustrating the use of the IF statement. Other statements would precede and follow this segment.

			FORTRAN STATEMENT	
			`IF (X - 2.1) 40, 40, 30`	
	40		`Y = 0.5 * X + 0.95`	
			`GO TO 45`	
	30		`Y = 0.7 * X + 0.53`	
	45		*Continuation*	

Figure 4.3. Another illustration of the use of the IF statement.

formula. Whatever appears at 45 could use the value of Y which now has been computed—by whichever method.

4.4 The Computed "GO TO" Statement

Still another kind of conditional transfer of control is provided. The computed GO TO statement is useful when it is desired to transfer control to one of a number of statements, depending upon the present value of some fixed point variable. The statement has the general form

$$GO\ TO\ (n_1, n_2, \cdots, n_m), i$$

In this statement i must be a fixed point variable written without a sign, and n_1, n_2, $\cdots$, n_m must be statement numbers. If the value of the variable i at the time this statement is executed is j, then control is transferred to the statement with the statement number n_j. For instance, suppose we have written the statement

$$GO\ TO\ (4, 600, 13, 9, 526), IAC$$

If the value of the variable IAC is 1, then control will be transferred to statement number 4; if it is 2, to statement 600, if it is 3, to statement 13, etc. The value of the fixed point variable must be in the range of 1 to m, where m is the quantity of statement numbers appearing in parentheses. If it is not in this range, the results are not predicted; in other words, we do not know in general what the program will do.

As an example of one kind of calculation that can be done with the computed GO TO statement, consider another problem. We are required, at a certain point in a program, to compute one of the first five Legendre polynomials according to the value of a fixed point variable LEG. These are defined as follows:

$$\text{If } LEG = 0, P_0(X) = 1$$
$$= 1, P_1(X) = X$$
$$= 2, P_2(X) = \tfrac{3}{2}X^2 - \tfrac{1}{2}$$
$$= 3, P_3(X) = \tfrac{5}{2}X^3 - \tfrac{3}{2}X$$
$$= 4, P_4(X) = \tfrac{35}{8}X^4 - \tfrac{15}{4}X^2 + \tfrac{3}{8}$$

Assume that X has been previously computed and that it has also been determined which of these five functions of X is to be computed, that is, that the value of LEG has been established. We cannot use the computed GO TO statement directly because of the restriction that the value of the fixed point variable must not be less than 1. Therefore, we shall first add 1 to LEG to make it fall in the range of 1 to 5 instead of 0 to 4. A program for carrying out this computation is shown in Figure 4.4. P is the name of whichever Legendre polynomial is computed.

The *assigned GO TO* statement accomplishes the same thing as the computed GO TO but in a slightly different way. This statement, which is available only on the larger versions of FORTRAN, is not sufficiently different to warrant discussion, for our purposes here.

4.5 Block Diagramming

One of the important tools of programming is the *block diagram*, or *flow chart*, which allows the programmer to plan the sequence of operations within a program *before* writing it. In a problem that is even moderately complex the interrelationships within the program become difficult to keep clearly in mind without some visual representation. A block diagram provides this visual assistance. It also greatly facilitates communication between programmers and is a valuable part of the documentation of a program.

A block diagram is made up of a set of blocks, the shape of which indicates the nature of the computer operation described in the block, along with lines and arrows that show the flow of control between the various operations.

For our purposes here the notation can be quite simple and will involve only the following symbols:

A rectangular box indicates any processing operation except a decision.

A diamond indicates a decision. The lines leaving the decision box are labeled with the decision result which causes each path to be followed.

A square box indicates a starting or stopping point of a program.

A small circle indicates a connection between two points in a block diagram, where a connecting line would be too clumsy.

Arrows indicate the direction of flow through the diagram; every connecting line should have an arrow on it.

An oval box indicates an input or output operation.

To illustrate how a block diagram may be used, we shall work out another problem involving the IF statement. Suppose we are required simply to read a value of X, perform certain checking on X, and compute a value of Y from these equations:

$$Y = \begin{cases} 8.72 & \text{if } 0.0 \le X < 10.9 \\ 16.19 & \text{if } 10.9 \le X < 21.6 \\ 24.07 & \text{if } 21.6 \le X < 50.0 \end{cases}$$

If $X < 0.0$ or $X \ge 50.0$, stop without computing Y.

A block diagram of the procedure for doing this job is shown in Figure 4.5. Notice that a colon in a decision box denotes a comparison, the precise nature of which is then shown on the lines leaving the box. The error stop is shown as "Stop 1" and the normal stop as "Stop 2." We might want to be able to tell from the console lights which stop caused the halt; 1 and 2 are for this purpose. The program is shown in Figure 4.6.

A small problem such as this does not really bring out the power of a block diagram. Even

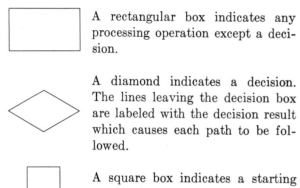

Figure 4.4. Program segment using the computed GO TO to select one of five formulas, depending on the value of a fixed point variable.

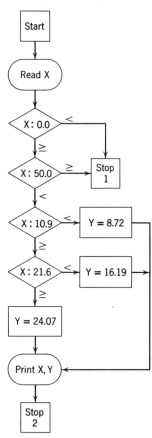

Figure 4.5. Block diagram of the program in Figure 4.6.

here, though, it can be seen that the sequence of tests is much clearer than if the procedure were described in words. In complex problems it becomes almost impossible to keep track of what is going on without a block diagram. It is strongly recommended that the reader become familiar with the technique and use it faithfully.

Note. The reader now has adequate background for Case Studies 1 and 5.

EXERCISES

Note. Some of the following exercises call for writing a few statements that would be a small segment of a larger program. It is not required to write any statements besides those necessary to satisfy the exercise. In each exercise draw a block diagram and write a program.

*1. Place whichever of the variables X and Y is algebraically larger in BIG. (For practice, do not use the special function available in some systems to do this automatically!) If X = Y, place *either* of them in BIG.

2. Place whichever of the variables X, Y, and Z is algebraically largest in BIG3. (This can be done with only two IF statements. Establish which of X and Y is larger, place it in a temporary location, and then compare this number with Z to find the largest of the three.)

3. The variables named R and S may be positive or negative. Place the one that is larger *in absolute value* in BIGAB. (The absolute value function, ABSF, gives

```
        READ 18, X
18      FORMAT (F10.0)
        IF (X) 20, 21, 21
21      IF (X - 50.) 22, 20, 20
20      STOP 1
22      IF (X - 10.9) 23, 24, 24
23      Y = 8.72
        GO TO 30
24      IF (X - 21.6) 25, 26, 26
25      Y = 16.19
        GO TO 30
26      Y = 24.07
30      PRINT 19, X, Y
19      FORMAT (2E20.8)
        STOP 2
        END
```

Figure 4.6. Program of the formula evaluation procedure block diagrammed in Figure 4.5.

the absolute value of its argument: the value of ABSF(R) is the absolute value of R, etc.)

*4. An angle named THETA is known to be positive and less than 30 radians. Subtract 2π from THETA as many times as necessary to reduce it to an angle less than 2π; leave the reduced angle in THETA.

*5. XREAL and XIMAG are the real and imaginary parts of a complex number. If the real and imaginary parts are *both* less than one in absolute value, transfer to statement 81; otherwise transfer to statement 82.

6. Y1, Y2, and Y3 are the ordinates of three points on a curve. If Y2 is a *local maximum*, that is, if Y2 > Y1 *and* Y2 > Y3, transfer to statement 456, otherwise to 567.

7. If DENOM is less than 10^{-5} *in absolute value*, transfer to statement 50; if it is greater than or equal to 10^{-5} in absolute value, transfer to statement 51. Write a program segment to do this:

a. without using the ABSF function;
b. using the ABSF function.

*8. If $0.999 \leq X \leq 1.001$, transfer to statement 63; otherwise transfer to statement 67. Write statements to do this:

a. using two IF statements, without using the ABSF function;
b. using one IF statement, the expression of which contains the ABSF function.

*9. If I = 1 and R < S, transfer to statement 261; if I = 1 and R $\geq$ S, transfer to statement 257; if I $\neq$ 1, transfer to statement 297.

10. If N = 1, 2, or 8, transfer to statement 250; if N = 3 or 7, transfer to statement 251; if N = 4, 5, or 6, transfer to statement 252; if N is not equal to any of these, transfer to statement 9999.

11. At a certain point in a program it is necessary to transfer to

a. statement 600   if I = 1
b. statement 607   if 1 < I < N
c. statement 619   if I = N

It may be assumed that I is never less than 1 nor greater than N. N is reasonably large, so that a computed GO TO cannot be used.

*12. Y is to be computed as a function of X according to

$$Y = 16.7X + 9.2X^2 - 1.02X^3$$

for X values from 1.0 to 9.9 in steps of 0.1. Print X and Y for each of the 90 values of X.

13. Y is to be computed as a function of X according to the formula

$$Y = \sqrt{1 + X} + \frac{\cos 2X}{1 + \sqrt{X}}$$

for a number of equally spaced values of X. Three numbers are to be read from a card: XINIT, XINC, and XFIN. Y is to be computed and printed initially for X = XINIT. Then X is to be incremented by XINC and Y computed and printed for this new value of X, and so on, until Y has been computed for the largest value of X not exceeding XFIN.

5. SUBSCRIPTED VARIABLES

5.1   Definitions

Subscripted variables permit us to represent many quantities with one variable name. A particular value is indicated by writing a subscript (or subscripts) in parentheses following the variable name. The complete set of quantities is called an *array,* and the individual quantities are called *elements.* A subscripted variable may have one, two, or three subscripts, and it then represents a one-, two-, or three-dimensional array, respectively. (When used in this connection, one-dimensional, etc., refers to the number of *subscripts,* not to the number of *elements:* a one-dimensional array can have many elements, and a three-dimensional array could in principle have only one element.)

The first element of a one-dimensional array is number 1, the second is number 2, etc., up to the number of elements in the array. In mathematical notation we might write $X_1, X_2, X_3, \cdots, X_{19}, X_{20}$; in FORTRAN subscript notation we would write $X(1)$, $X(2), X(3), \cdots, X(19), X(20)$.

A two-dimensional array may be thought of as being composed of horizontal rows and vertical columns. The first of the two subscripts then refers to the *row number,* running from 1 up to the number of rows, and the second to the *column number,* running from 1 up to the number of columns. For instance, an array of two rows and three columns might be shown in mathematical notation as

$$A_{1,1} \quad A_{1,2} \quad A_{1,3}$$
$$A_{2,1} \quad A_{2,2} \quad A_{2,3}$$

In FORTRAN subscript notation the elements would be written $A(1,1)$, $A(2,1)$, $A(1,2)$, $A(2,2)$, $A(1,3)$, $A(2,3)$. We note that the subscripts are separated by commas, as they are in three-dimensional variables.

A three-dimensional array may be thought of, if one wishes, as being composed of planes, each plane containing rows and columns. Its interpretation, however, depends somewhat on the purpose of the computation; other interpretations are possible.

The name of a subscripted variable must not end in F, but the naming is otherwise the same as in nonsubscripted variables. In particular, an array may consist of either fixed or floating point elements, and the meaning of the first character of the name is the same as in single variables. The elements of any one array, however, must be *all* fixed point or *all* floating point.

5.2   Examples of the Subscript Notation

Suppose we have two points in space, represented in coordinate form by $X_1, X_2,$ X_3 and Y_1, Y_2, Y_3. We are required to compute the distance between them, which is given by

$$D = \sqrt{(X_1 - Y_1)^2 + (X_2 - Y_2)^2 + (X_3 - Y_3)^2}$$

Now suppose that we have set up an array called X, the three elements of which are the floating point coordinates of the point X, and another similarly for Y. The computation of the distance between the points can

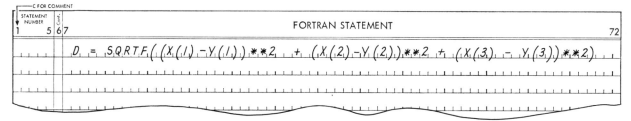

Figure 5.1. An example of the use of the subscript notation.

be called for by the statement shown in Figure 5.1.

It may be well to review the four uses of parentheses in FORTRAN, all but one of which are illustrated here.

1. Parentheses indicate grouping for arithmetic operations.

2. They enclose the argument of a function.

3. They enclose the subscript or subscripts of a subscripted variable.

4. They enclose the field specifications in a FORMAT statement.

For another example of the subscript notation consider the problem of solving two simultaneous linear algebraic equations in two unknowns. To emphasize the similarity of subscripted variables with mathematical notation, we may write the system of equations completely in mathematical subscript form.

$$C_{1,1}X_1 + C_{1,2}X_2 = B_1$$

$$C_{2,1}X_1 + C_{2,2}X_2 = B_2$$

This problem can conveniently be set up with a one-dimensional array of two elements for the constant terms B_1 and B_2, and another for the unknowns, X_1 and X_2, which we will compute. The coefficients (C's) will be the four elements of a two-dimensional array of two rows and two columns.

The solution of such a small system of equations

can be done conveniently by Cramer's rule, according to which

$$X_1 = \frac{B_1 \cdot C_{2,2} - B_2 \cdot C_{1,2}}{C_{1,1} \cdot C_{2,2} - C_{2,1} \cdot C_{1,2}}$$

$$X_2 = \frac{B_2 \cdot C_{1,1} - B_1 \cdot C_{2,1}}{C_{1,1} \cdot C_{2,2} - C_{2,1} \cdot C_{1,2}}$$

A program to evaluate these formulas is shown in Figure 5.2, in which we have done two things that should be explained. First, since the denominator of both expressions is the same, it is computed first and used in computing both X_1 and X_2. Second, there is a possibility that this denominator will be zero, indicating either no solution or an infinite number of solutions, depending on the constant terms. Either way, Cramer's rule obviously does not apply, since a division by zero would be required. If a division by zero is attempted, some sort of error indication is given, the nature of which depends on the machine being used. The program should therefore include a test for this possibility.

Actually, we need to do a little more than just test the denominator for zero. Because of rounding and the truncation errors mentioned on p. 13, the denominator could be very small—indicating trouble or at least indicating inaccurate results—without actually being zero. We should therefore determine whether the absolute value of the de-

```
DENØM = C(1,1)*C(2,2) - C(2,1)*C(1,2)
      IF(ABSF(DENØM) - 1.E-5) 50, 51, 51
50    STØP
51    X(1) = (B(1)*C(2,2) - B(2)*C(1,2))/DENØM
      X(2) = (B(2)*C(1,1) - B(1)*C(2,1))/DENØM
```

Figure 5.2. Program segment using subscripting to solve two simultaneous equations.

nominator is less than some small number, say 10^{-5}.

5.3 Motivations for the Use of Subscripted Variables

The foregoing examples show the fundamental ideas of the subscript notation, but they do not really indicate the power of the technique. After all, there is nothing in the examples that could not be done just as conveniently by giving each variable a separate name. Why then are subscripted variables such an important feature of FORTRAN?

The reason is that the subscripts may themselves be variables or certain types of expressions. This means that we can set up a program to perform a basic computation, then make the same computation on many different values simply by changing the value of the subscript.

Suppose, for instance, that we need to compute the sum of the squares of 20 numbers, X_1 to X_{20}, that are stored in the computer. We could, of course, give them 20 different names and set up a long arithmetic statement to compute the sum of their squares, but this would be tedious, cumbersome, and inflexible. Instead, we set up the 20 numbers as the elements of a one-dimensional array which we call X. Now, any of the 20 can be referenced by the name $X(I)$, and we arrange for I to take on all the values from 1 to 20.

The usual mathematical notation for this operation is

$$SUMSQ = \sum_{i=1}^{20} X_i^2$$

The computation can be done with the program shown in Figure 5.3. We first set SUMSQ equal to zero so that we may use a single expression to compute each of the intermediate sums. Then I is made 1 so that when statement 180 is first executed we get the first element from the array of values. Then 1 is added to I and a test is made to determine whether all of the values have been used. Note that when the IF shows that $I = 20$, we must still go back once more because I is modified *before the test*.

The last three statements in this program are executed exactly 20 times to give the sum of the squares of the 20 elements of the array. We shall see in Chapter 6 that this program can be made even simpler by using a DO statement. In actual practice we would seldom write it as shown above.

5.4 The DIMENSION Statement and Other Information

When subscripted variables are used in a program, certain information about them must be supplied to FORTRAN:

1. Which variables are subscripted?
2. How many subscripts are there for each subscripted variable?
3. How many elements are there in each array, that is, what is the maximum size of each subscript?

These questions are answered by the DIMENSION statement. Every subscripted variable in a program must be mentioned in a DIMENSION statement, and this statement must appear before the first occurrence of a variable in the program. A common practice is to give the dimension information for all subscripted variables in a DIMENSION statement at the start of the program. One DIMENSION statement may mention any number

```
C FOR COMMENT
STATEMENT
NUMBER    Cont.
1      5 6 7                    FORTRAN STATEMENT                        72

          SUMSQ = 0.0
          I = 1
   180    SUMSQ = SUMSQ + X(I)**2
          I = I + 1
          IF (I - 20) 180, 180, 181
   181
```

Figure 5.3. Program segment using subscripting and the IF statement to compute the sum of the squares of 20 numbers.

of variables, and there may be any number of statements.

The DIMENSION statement is of the form

DIMENSION V, V, V, $\cdots$

where the V's stand for variable names followed by parentheses enclosing one, two, or three unsigned fixed point constants which give the maximum size of each subscript. When FORTRAN processes a DIMENSION statement, it sets aside enough storage locations to contain arrays of the sizes defined by the information in the statement. Thus, if a program contains the statement

DIMENSION X(20), A(3, 10), K(2, 2, 5)

FORTRAN will assign 20 locations to the one-dimensional array named X; 30 (3×10) to the two-dimensional A array; and 20 ($2 \times 2 \times 5$) to the three-dimensional K array.

It is the programmer's responsibility to write the program so that no subscript is ever larger than the maximum size specified in the DIMENSION statement. Furthermore, subscripts must never be smaller than 1; zero and negative subscripts are not permitted. If these restrictions are violated, the source program will be compiled, but the object program will in all probability give incorrect results.

The DIMENSION statement is said to be *non-executable*, that is, it provides information only to the FORTRAN processor and does not result in the creation of any instructions in the object program. It may therefore appear anywhere in the source program, even between two arithmetic statements. As previously noted, however, the dimension information for each subscripted variable must be given before the first appearance of that variable. Furthermore, a DIMENSION statement must not be the first statement in the range of a DO statement (see Chapter 6).

Subscripted variables, with a few exceptions noted later, may appear in any place in which an unsubscripted variable may be written. For a simple example consider the READ statement that might be used to read in the data for the simultaneous equations example in Section 5.2. The DIMENSION, READ, and FORMAT statements for that problem could be

DIMENSION B(2), C(2, 2), X(2)
READ 16, C(1, 1), C(2, 1), C(1, 2), C(2, 2), B(1), B(2)
16 FORMAT (6F10.0)

The "6" in front of the field specification (F10.0) means that there are six fields all having the same format.

When a READ statement is written with the elements indicated in this explicit form, the elements may be entered in any sequence desired. The programmer might choose, for instance, to write

READ 16, C(1, 1), C(1, 2), B(1), C(2, 1), C(2, 2), B(2)

The data would naturally have to be punched on the data card in the corresponding order, but otherwise the sequence makes no difference—as long as the elements are named explicitly.

However, we occasionally wish to deal with the elements of an array *without* explicitly naming them all. It is permissible to use an input or output statement in which the name of an array is written without any subscripting information; this will call for the reading or writing of the entire array. Thus we could follow the DIMENSION statement in the example above with

READ 16, C, B

to read all of the elements of the two arrays.

It is, of course, necessary in such a case to have a convention regarding the sequence of the elements, since we are not giving FORTRAN the sequence we desire. The sequence in which the elements must appear on the card in order to use an input or output statement that does not give subscripting information is as follows. For one-dimensional arrays, the elements are taken in sequence, starting with the element corresponding to the subscript 1 and proceeding to the largest subscript as defined in the DIMENSION statement. For two-dimensional arrays the elements are taken in such a manner that the first subscript varies most rapidly. Thus the statements

DIMENSION R(2, 3)
READ 16, R

would require that the elements be punched in the sequence R(1, 1), R(2, 1), R(1, 2), R(2, 2), R(1, 3), R(2, 3). This can be summarized by saying that the elements of a two-dimensional array are taken in *column-order*. For three-dimensional arrays the elements are taken in such a manner that the first subscript varies most rapidly and the last subscript varies least rapidly.

5.5 Allowable Forms of Subscripts

So far we have seen that subscripts may be fixed point constants or fixed point variables. Three other forms of subscripts are permitted. If V stands for a fixed point variable and if C and C' are fixed point constants, then all of the allowable forms of subscripts are

$$C$$

$$V$$

$$V \pm C$$

$$C*V$$

$$C*V \pm C'$$

The value of the subscript expression, even without the added or subtracted constant, if any, must never be less than 1 nor greater than the maximum specified in a DIMENSION statement. The variables in a subscript must not themselves be subscripted.

There are many situations in which the last three forms of subscripts find application. We may illustrate the use of one of these forms in an example that can be done in two different but equivalent ways.

Suppose that at a certain point in a program the following computation is required:

$$y = \begin{cases} a + bX + cX^2 & \text{if } K = 1 \\ d + eX + fX^2 & \text{if } K = 2 \\ g + hX + iX^2 & \text{if } K = 3 \end{cases}$$

The values of K and X have previously been established. We know how to write three statements with the different coefficients and then use a computed GO TO to pick the appropriate statement. The procedure, however, is much simpler with subscripting.

Suppose we make the nine coefficients the elements of a one-dimensional array which we may call C:

a b c d e f g h i

1 2 3 4 5 6 7 8 9

If K = 1, the numbers of the desired elements are

$$1 = 3K - 2$$

$$2 = 3K - 1$$

$$3 = 3K$$

If K = 2, the numbers of the desired elements are

$$4 = 3K - 2$$

$$5 = 3K - 1$$

$$6 = 3K$$

If K = 3, the numbers are

$$7 = 3K - 2$$

$$8 = 3K - 1$$

$$9 = 3K$$

Thus, for any value of K, the proper coefficients will be used if we write

$$Y = C(3*K - 2) + C(3*K - 1)*X + C(3*K)*X**2$$

If the coefficients had been arranged thus,

a d g b e h c f i

1 2 3 4 5 6 7 8 9

the statement would have been

$$Y = C(K) + C(K + 3)*X + C(K + 6)*X**2$$

Another approach, which gives the same results, is to make the coefficients the elements of a two-dimensional array:

a b c

d e f

g h i

In this array K can be used to select the proper row (first subscript), and 1, 2, or 3 can be used to select the proper column (second subscript). The arithmetic statement now becomes

$$Y = C(K, 1) + C(K, 2)*X + C(K, 3)*X**2$$

Thus we see that subscripted variables facilitate the selection of one set of data from a larger set. We also see that the elements of an array, in contrast to ordinary mathematical usage, are not required to have any special relationships to each other.

Still, the most common use of subscripted variables is in carrying out the same computation on a set of related quantities. We shall see several more examples of this usage in Chapter 6 on the DO statement.

EXERCISES

Note. Include an appropriate DIMENSION statement in all programs for these exercises.

*1. The coordinates of a point in space are given by the three elements of a one-dimensional array named X. (Note the different usages of the word dimension: the elements of a one-dimensional array are being used as the coordinates of a point in three-dimensional space!) Write a statement to compute the distance of the point from the origin, which is given by the square root of the sum of the squares of the coordinates.

2. If the coordinates of a point in space are X_1, X_2, X_3, the direction cosines of the line from the origin to the point are given by

$$CA = \frac{X_1}{\sqrt{X_1{}^2 + X_2{}^2 + X_3{}^2}}$$

$$CB = \frac{X_2}{\sqrt{X_1{}^2 + X_2{}^2 + X_3{}^2}}$$

$$CC = \frac{X_3}{\sqrt{X_1{}^2 + X_2{}^2 + X_3{}^2}}$$

Write statements to compute these three numbers, assuming that the coordinates are the elements of a one-dimensional array named X.

*3. Given two arrays A and B, both two-dimensional, write statements to compute the elements of another two-dimensional array named C, from the following equations. The maximum value of all subscripts is 2.

$$c_{11} = a_{11} \cdot b_{11} + a_{12} \cdot b_{21}$$

$$c_{12} = a_{11} \cdot b_{12} + a_{12} \cdot b_{22}$$

$$c_{21} = a_{21} \cdot b_{11} + a_{22} \cdot b_{21}$$

$$c_{22} = a_{21} \cdot b_{12} + a_{22} \cdot b_{22}$$

(Multiplication of two 2×2 matrices.)

4. Given a two-dimensional array named R, the elements of which are to be viewed as the elements of a 3×3 determinant, write a statement to compute the value of the determinant, which should be named DET.

*5. Two one-dimensional arrays named A and B each contain 30 elements. Compute

$$D = \left(\sum_{i=1}^{30} (A_i - B_i)^2 \right)^{1/2}$$

*6. A one-dimensional array named X contains 50 elements. Compute the 49 elements of another array named DX, according to

$$DX(I) = X(I + 1) - X(I), \qquad I = 1, 2, 3, \cdots, 49$$

7. A one-dimensional array Y contains 32 elements. Compute

$$TRAP = Y_1 + 2Y_2 + 2Y_3 + \cdots + 2Y_{30} + 2Y_{31} + Y_{32}$$

8. A two-dimensional array named AMATR contains 10 rows and 10 columns. A one-dimensional array named DIAG contains 10 elements. Compute the elements of DIAG from the formula

$$DIAG(i) = AMATR(i, i), \qquad i = 1, 2, \cdots, 10$$

*9. Given a one-dimensional array named Y, with 50 elements, and numbers U and I, write a statement to compute the value of S from the following equation, written in ordinary mathematical subscript notation:

$$S = y_i + u \frac{y_{i+1} - y_{i-1}}{2} + \frac{u^2}{2} (y_{i+1} - 2y_i + y_{i-1})$$

(Stirling's interpolation formula, through third differences.)

10. Using the assumptions in Exercise 9, write a statement to compute the value of T from the following equation:

$$T = y_i + u(y_{i+1} - y_i) + \frac{u(u-1)(y_{i+2} - y_{i+1} - y_i + y_{i-1})}{4}$$

$$+ \frac{(u - \frac{1}{2})u(u - 1)(y_{i+2} - 3y_{i+1} + 3y_i - y_{i-1})}{6}$$

*11. Given two one-dimensional arrays named A and B, of seven elements each, suppose that the seven elements of the A array are punched on one card and the seven values of the B array are punched on a second card. Write a program to read the cards, then compute and punch the value of ANORM from the definition

$$ANORM = \sqrt{\sum_{i=1}^{7} a_i b_i}$$

12. Using the assumptions in Exercise 11, write a program to read the data cards and then carry out the following procedure. If every $a_i > b_i$, for $i = 1, 2, \cdots, 7$, then punch a 1 on a card; if this condition is not satisfied, punch a zero on a card.

6. THE **DO** STATEMENT

6.1 Introduction

A most powerful feature of the FORTRAN language is the DO statement. This statement makes it possible to carry out a section of a program repeatedly, with changes in the value of a fixed point variable between repetitions. Coupled with subscripted variables, the DO statement provides a simple way to make calculations that are quite complicated when done with actual machine instructions. In view of the importance of this topic, we shall show its application in several examples.

The DO statement may be written in either of the forms

$$DO\ n\ i = m_1, m_2$$

or

$$DO\ n\ i = m_1, m_2, m_3$$

In the statement n must be a statement number, i must be a nonsubscripted fixed point variable, written without a sign, and m_1, m_2, and m_3 must each be either an unsigned fixed point constant or a nonsubscripted fixed point variable. If m_3 is not stated, as in the first form of the statement, it is understood to be 1. The statements following the DO, up to and including the statement with the number n, are executed repeatedly. They are executed first with $i = m_1$; before each succeeding execution i is increased by m_3; repeated execution continues until the statements have been executed with i equal to the largest value not exceeding m_2.

To illustrate how the DO statement works and how it may be used, let us consider again the problem stated in connection with sub-scripting on p. 32. It will be recalled that we were required to form the sum of the squares of the 20 elements of a one-dimensional array named X. This can be done with the short program shown in Figure 6.1.

The DIMENSION statement establishes X as a subscripted variable having one subscript, the maximum value of which is 20. We first set the sum location to zero, then go into the DO statement. This says to execute repeatedly all the statements following the DO, down to and including the one numbered 180. There is, of course, only one statement in this range, and statement 180 itself is the repeated part. Statement 180 is carried out first with $I = 1$, so that the first time through we get X_1^2 in SUMSQ. Then I is increased by 1 and statement 180 executed again, this time adding X_2^2 to the X_1^2 which is already in SUMSQ. This process is repeated until statement 180 has been executed with $I = 20$, after which SUMSQ contains the sum of the squares of all 20 numbers. Control then passes on to the statement following 180.

For another example of a DO statement, suppose that we have a one-dimensional array called DATA which contains 21 elements. We wish to form the sum of all of the odd-numbered elements and to place this sum in a location we call SUM. The program of Figure 6.2 will do this.

The DO statement, in this case, says to execute the statement numbered 500 with J equal to $1, 3, 5, \cdots, 17, 19, 21$. The first time statement 500 is executed the value of the variable SUM is zero, so that the net effect is to move the first element of DATA to

```
C FOR COMMENT
STATEMENT
NUMBER        FORTRAN STATEMENT
1        5 6 7                                                          72

          DIMENSION X (20)
          SUMSQ = 0.0
          DO 180 I = 1, 20
   180    SUMSQ = SUMSQ + X(I)**2
```

Figure 6.1. A program using a DO loop to form the sum of the squares of 20 numbers.

SUM. The second time it is executed the net effect is to add to this the value of the third element of DATA, etc. When it has been executed with J equal to 21, which adds in the last element, then control passes on to the statement following statement 500, whatever that may be.

6.2 Further Definitions

Before proceeding to more examples, we present a few definitions that will make it easier to talk about the DO statement. The *range* of the DO statement is the set of repeatedly executed statements. In short, it consists of the statements beginning with the one immediately following the DO and continuing up to and including the statement named in the DO. The fixed point variable i in the general form of the DO statement is called its *index*. Throughout the execution of the range, i is available for any purpose permitted for a fixed point variable. We have seen how it may be used as a subscript and shall see later how it can be applied in other ways.

There are two general methods by which control can transfer outside the range of a DO. The *nor-*

mal exit occurs when the DO is *satisfied*, that is, at the completion of the number of executions of the range as specified by the *indexing parameters* m_1, m_2, and m_3. When this happens, as we have seen, control passes to the statement following the one named in the DO. The second method by which control can get outside the range of a DO is through a GO TO or IF statement. This can happen when it is desired to specify (in the DO parameters) the *maximum* number of executions of the range, but to set up tests in the range to determine the *actual* number of executions.

When control is transferred outside the range of a DO *before* the DO is satisfied, the index i is available for any purpose permitted for a fixed point variable. This can be quite valuable. After the normal exit, i is *not* available (at least not in most versions of FORTRAN).

To examine another way in which the index of a DO may be used within the range, consider the following example. In a problem involving combinations we are required to form the product of all integers from 1 to M, wherein the value of M has been determined earlier in the program. By naming the variable M, we indicate, of course, that it is a *fixed point* variable; we wish, however, to

```
C FOR COMMENT
STATEMENT
NUMBER        FORTRAN STATEMENT
1        5 6 7                                                          72

          DIMENSION DATA (21)
          SUM = 0.0
          DO 500 J = 1, 21, 2
   500    SUM = SUM + DATA (J)
```

Figure 6.2. A program to form the sum of the odd-numbered elements of an array.

STATEMENT NUMBER	Cont.	FORTRAN STATEMENT	
1 5	6 7		72
		PRØD = 1.0	
		DØ 6 I = 2, M	
		AI = I	
6		PRØD = PRØD * AI	

C FOR COMMENT

Figure 6.3. A program to form the product of the integers from 1 to M.

obtain the product in a floating point form. In order to avoid the complications of possibly computing too large a fixed point number within the DO loop, we must convert each of the factors in the product from fixed point to floating point. The program of Figure 6.3 does all this and places the product in a location called PROD. We first set PROD equal to 1.0 and then go into the DO loop, asking for the range to be executed with I equal to all values from 2 to M. In order to use the index I in a floating point calculation, we execute the statement AI = I, which, as we recall from earlier rules, calls for the conversion of I to floating point form. The first time statement 6 is executed, the effect is to multiply 1.0 by 2.0 (since PROD has been started at 1.0) and to store the product in PROD. The next time, this product is multiplied by 3.0 and the new product is stored back in PROD. The process continues until the two statements in the range have been executed with I equal to M.

Implicit in this program is the assumption that M is at least 2. If M could be 1, the DO statement would ask for the range to be executed with I equal to all values from 2 up to 1, which, of course, is impossible. What the DO statement would do in such a case cannot be stated in general. If M were equal to 2, the program would not get into trouble: the two statements in the range would be executed exactly once and control would then pass to the statement following 6.

This example shows that it is important to be sure that the range of a DO is executed exactly the right number of times. Experience shows that it is all too easy to make mistakes on this point. A good way to check is to ask, "What would the parameters have to be if the range were to be executed only *once?*" Based on this, it is usually not too difficult to decide if the actual situation is properly handled.

6.3 Rules Governing the Use of the DO Statement

A great deal of flexibility is permitted in the use of the DO statement as long as certain rules are observed. We shall state all of these rules together and later illustrate the situations that some of them cover.

Rule 1. The first statement in the range of a DO must be a statement that can be executed. This excludes the DIMENSION and FORMAT statements, since, rather than causing anything to happen in the object program, they simply provide information to the compiler. As we shall see later, several other statements are also nonexecutable.

Rule 2. It is permissible for the range of one DO (which we may call the "outer" DO) to contain another DO (which we may call the "inner" DO). When this occurs, it is required that all statements in the range of the inner DO also be in the range of the outer DO. This does not prohibit the ranges of two or more DO's ending with the same statement, but it does prohibit a situation in which the range of an inner DO extends past the end of the range of an outer DO.

Rule 3. The last statement in the range of a DO must not be one that can cause a transfer of control. This excludes the GO TO, the computed GO TO, the IF, and the DO statements. These statements may be used freely anywhere else in the range. The CONTINUE statement described below is provided for situations that would otherwise violate this rule.

Rule 4. No statement within the range of a DO may redefine or otherwise alter any of the indexing parameters of that DO, that is, it is not permitted within the range of a DO to change the values of i, m_1, m_2, or m_3. As noted before, these numbers may still be used in any way that does not alter their values.

Rule 5. Control must not transfer into the range of a DO from any statement outside its range, with one exception. Thus it is expressly prohibited to use a GO TO or an IF statement to transfer into the range of a DO without first executing the DO itself. This rule *does* prohibit a transfer from the range of an outer DO into the range of an inner DO, but it *does not* prohibit a transfer out of the range of an inner DO into the range of an outer DO. The latter is permissible because, from the standpoint of the outer DO, the transfer is executed entirely within its range. Some illustrations of this rule are provided in Figure 6.4. The brackets here represent the ranges of DO's and the arrows represent transfers of control. Transfers 2, 3, and 4 are acceptable, since 2 and 3 are transfers from the range of an inner DO to the range of an outer DO, and 4 is a transfer entirely within the range of a single DO. Transfers 1, 5, and 6 all represent transfers into the range of a DO from outside its range. The one exception to the rule prohibiting transfers into the range of a DO from outside its range is this: it is permissible to transfer control completely outside the nest to which a DO belongs, perform a series of calculations which makes no changes in any of the indices or indexing parameters in the nest, and then transfer back to the range of the same DO from which transfer was originally made. The restriction on the exit and re-entry transfer locations may be stated another way: no DO, and no statement which is the last statement in the range of a DO, may lie between the exit and re-entry points.

CONTINUE is a dummy statement that causes no action when the object program is executed. It merely satisfies the rule that the last statement in the range of a DO must not be one that can cause transfer of control. It is also used to provide a statement to which an IF can transfer when the computations in the range of a DO have been completed. This is necessary because a transfer within the range of a DO is not permitted to return to the DO itself, that is, not unless it is really intended to start the execution of the DO from the beginning again. An example of the use of the CONTINUE statement appears in Section 6.4.

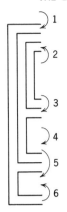

Figure 6.4. Examples of permissible nests of DO's and some correct and incorrect transfers of control. Transfers 2, 3, and 4 are acceptable; 1, 5, and 6 are not.

6.4 Further Examples of the Use of the DO Statement

Since the DO statement is so powerful and since it is so heavily used in most FORTRAN applications, we shall give some additional examples of its use.

For the first of these examples suppose that the input to a program consists of a series of experimentally measured values. Each point in the experiment involves an X value and a Y value, corresponding to the abscissa and ordinate on a graph. The data points were gathered and entered into the computer in random order; that is, we know that the first X value goes with the first Y value and that the second X value goes with the second Y value, etc., but we cannot assume that the first X value is the smallest of all of the X values. For the purposes of calculations that are to be done later in the program, it is necessary to rearrange the data points in storage so that the first X value *is* the smallest and that the second X value is the next larger, and so on. In other words, we must order the data points into ascending sequence on the X values.

We shall assume that the X values as they were originally read (i.e., in scrambled order) are the elements of an array named X and that there are 25 of them. The Y values are the elements of another array called Y which also contains 25 values.

The FORTRAN program to rearrange these data points into ascending sequence on the X values involves a nest of two DO loops. We shall show the development of the program, however, by displaying a simplified version of the inner loop before writing the entire program. This simplified loop will place the smallest X value in the first position of the X array. This can be done by the following process. First compare the first and second X values in the original array. If the first X is smaller than or equal to the second, leave them alone; if the first X is larger than the second, interchange these two values within the array. Having inspected the first and second elements and interchanged them if necessary, inspect the first and third elements and either leave them alone or interchange them if the first element is the larger. This "first" element may very well be the one that was originally in second position, but this does not matter. Similarly, compare the first and fourth, first and fifth, etc., until the element in the first position has been compared with all others, interchanging at each step if necessary. This process guarantees that the smallest X will end up in the first position of the X array. Remembering that to each X there corresponds a Y, we naturally carry out the same interchange operations on the Y array as we have on the X array, but there will be no testing of the Y values.

In order to interchange two values from the array in storage, we follow a three-step process: (1) move the first value to a temporary storage location which we call TEMP; (2) move the second value to the location originally occupied by the first; (3) move the first value, which is in TEMP, to the location originally occupied by the second.

A program to carry out all of this is shown in Figure 6.5. We are assuming that the data values have been read in by an earlier part of the program, and we are not showing the statements that complete the rearrangement or use the data values.

This program illustrates a number of features worth noting. We see another example of a DO loop in which the index does not start with 1. We see an example of the use of the CONTINUE statement. This is required, in this case, because if the IF statement shows that the first X value is already smaller than the other X value with which we are comparing it then a transfer of control is required in order to skip around the six statements that interchange the X and Y values involved. What we want to do in this case is simply to repeat the whole process again with the index J increased by 1. As we have already noted, however, it is not possible to transfer control back to the DO. This would result in starting the DO loop again with J equal to 2—which is not what we want. Therefore, we transfer control to CONTINUE, which has been identified in the DO statement as the end of the range.

In reading this program, it is well to recall the meaning of an arithmetic statement: the value of the variable on the left side of the equal sign is replaced by the value of the expression on the right. Thus a statement such as

$$X(1) = X(J)$$

means that the number identified by the variable name $X(J)$ is to be moved to the location for the number identified by the name $X(1)$. The value in the location $X(J)$ is unchanged.

```
      DIMENSION X(25), Y(25)
      DO 12 J = 2,25
      IF(X(1) - X(J)) 12, 12, 13
   13 TEMP = X(1)
      X(1) = X(J)
      X(J) = TEMP
      TEMP = Y(1)
      Y(1) = Y(J)
      Y(J) = TEMP
   12 CONTINUE
```

Figure 6.5. A program to place the smallest value of X in an array of X's in the first position of the array and to place the corresponding Y in the first position of an array of Y's.

```
---C FOR COMMENT
STATEMENT
 NUMBER      Cont.                    FORTRAN STATEMENT
1        5  6 7                                                                    72
         DIMENSION X(25), Y(25)
         DO 12 I = 1,24
         IP1 = I + 1
         DO 12 J = IP1,25
         IF(X(I) - X(J)) 12, 12, 13
      13 TEMP = X(I)
         X(I) = X(J)
         X(J) = TEMP
         TEMP = Y(I)
         Y(I) = Y(J)
         Y(J) = TEMP
      12 CONTINUE
```

Figure 6.6. A program to rearrange a set of X-Y data points into ascending sequence on the X values.

In the problem as stated there may or may not be two equal X values. As the program has been written, however, it does not matter; if they are equal, then there is no point in exchanging them and we simply transfer control down to CONTINUE and go around the loop again.

When this loop has been finished (when the DO has been "satisfied"), we are guaranteed that the data points have been rearranged so that the smallest X is in the first position in the X array and that the Y corresponding to the smallest X is in the first position in the Y array. What we would like to do next is to get the next larger X in the second position of the array. This can be done by comparing the second element with the third, and all following, and interchanging whenever necessary. After that we would like to get the next larger element in the third position. We would similarly arrange to get the next larger X values in the fourth, fifth positions, etc., until finally all of the X's have been placed in the X array in order of increasing size.

It appears then that what we need to do for the complete program is to make variables of all subscripts that appear as 1's. The subscript will then select the element to be compared with all following elements (interchanging if necessary). This subscript, which we shall call I, will start at 1 and run through 24. The subscript which appears as J in the present program will still appear as J, but it will have to start at one more than whatever the I subscript is and run to 25. All of

this is easily done by another DO statement that controls the I subscript. This is the outer DO. There is one complication, however. The inner DO must specify that the J subscript will start at one more than whatever I is. Looking back at the definition of the DO statement, we see that each indexing parameter must either be a fixed point constant or a single fixed point variable. It is not permissible to write a statement such as

$$\text{DO } 12 \text{ J} = \text{I} + 1, 25$$

To avoid this restriction, we simply insert a statement that computes the value of a variable IP1, which is always one more than whatever I is. The complete program to sort the data points is shown in Figure 6.6.

In order to illustrate a slightly different type of DO loop, let us now make some further assumptions about the purpose of the programs just written. Suppose that the data points which have been read in and by now arranged into ascending sequence lie on a curve and that we are required to find the area under this curve; that is, to find the definite integral of the curve represented approximately by these points. There are many formulas for numerical integration; we shall show programs for the trapezoidal rule and Simpson's rule. If we now make the further assumption that the distance between successive X points is equal to a constant value H, then the approximate integral given by the trapezoidal rule is

```
C FOR COMMENT
STATEMENT NUMBER          FORTRAN STATEMENT                                    72
1         5 6 7
          SUM = 0.0
          DO 20 I = 2,24
     20   SUM = SUM + Y(I)
          AREA = (X(2)-X(1))/2.*(Y(1)+2.*SUM+Y(25))
```

Figure 6.7. A program for integration by the trapezoidal rule.

$$AREA = \frac{H}{2}\{y_1 + 2y_2 + 2y_3 + \cdots + 2y_{23} + 2y_{24} + y_{25}\}$$

A DO loop may conveniently be used to form the sum of the Y values with subscripts of 2 through 24. Having done so, we can multiply this sum by 2, add the first and last Y values, and multiply by H/2. This program, shown in Figure 6.7, would follow the CONTINUE statement of the program shown in Figure 6.6.

This program includes the computation of H on the assumption that it is the interval between any two X values. If, in fact, the X values are not equally spaced, then the program naturally gives an incorrect result. If it were required that the program be able to handle unequally spaced X values, some other numerical integration method would have to be used.

Simpson's rule gives a more accurate approximation to the integral of the function represented by the data points:

$$AREA = \frac{H}{3}(y_1 + 4y_2 + 2y_3 + 4y_4 + 2y_5 + \cdots + 2y_{23} + 4y_{24} + y_{25})$$

A program to evaluate this formula will be a little more complex because of the alternating coefficients of 2 and 4. One fairly obvious way to handle the problem is to set up two DO loops and to accumulate separately the sums of the Y values corresponding to the two coefficients. See Figure 6.8.

The computation may be done with only one DO loop, which saves a little time in the running of the object program, if we proceed as follows. Suppose we set up an index that runs from 1 to 11. Two times that index will always be the subscript of a Y value that should be multiplied by 4, and two times that index plus 1 will always be the subscript of a Y value that should be multiplied by 2. See Figure 6.9.

Flexibility in the manner of writing subscripts is very useful here. It is not possible to form the sum of the Y values with one DO loop unless some such subscripting arrangement is used.

It may be noted that we have written these integration formulas with the subscripts starting with 1, whereas it is conventional to write them with the subscripts starting at 0. This was done to make it easier to describe the program, since we recall that a subscript must be positive and nonzero. It is possible to program formulas that have

```
C FOR COMMENT
STATEMENT NUMBER          FORTRAN STATEMENT                                    72
1         5 6 7
          ODD = 0.
          EVEN = 0.
          DO 47 I = 2,24,2
     47   EVEN = EVEN + Y(I)
          DO 48 I = 3,23,2
     48   ODD = ODD + Y(I)
          AREA = (X(2) - X(1))/3.*(Y(1) + 4.*EVEN + 2.*ODD + Y(25))
```

Figure 6.8. One version of a program for integration by Simpson's rule.

```
C FOR COMMENT
STATEMENT
NUMBER
1        5  6 7                    FORTRAN STATEMENT                           72

         SUM = 0.
         DO 51 I = 1, 11
    51   SUM = SUM + 4.*Y(2*I) + 2.*Y(2*I+1)
         AREA = (X(2)-X(1))/3.*(Y(1)+SUM+4.*Y(24)+Y(25))
```

Figure 6.9. A shorter version of a program for integration by Simpson's rule.

zero or negative subscripts, but somewhat more effort is required than is valuable to us at this point. (It may be noted that ALTAC, an algebraic compiler similar to FORTRAN used with the Philco 2000, does not have this restriction to positive nonzero subscripts.)

Note. The reader now has adequate background for Case Studies 1 to 6.

EXERCISES

Include a DIMENSION statement in all programs involving arrays. Use a DO statement in all cases.

*1. Write a program to form the sum of the 50 elements of a one-dimensional array named AX4 and place it in ASUM.

2. Two one-dimensional arrays named A and B contain 30 elements each. Compute

$$D = \left(\sum_{i=1}^{30} (A_i \cdot B_i)^2 \right)^{\frac{1}{2}}$$

*3. A one-dimensional fixed point array named M contains 20 elements. Write a program to replace each element by itself, multiplied by its element number. In other words, replace m_i by $i \cdot m_i$, $i = 1, 2, \cdots, 20$.

4. A one-dimensional array named X contains 50 elements. Write a loop to compute the 49 elements of another array named DX, according to

$$DX(I) = X(I+1) - X(I), I = 1, 2, 3, \cdots, 49$$

*5. Two one-dimensional arrays named R and S have a *maximum* of 40 elements each. The *actual* number of elements is given by the value of the previously computed fixed point variable M. Compute the first M elements of an array named T, which also has a maximum of 40 elements, according to

$$T(i) = R(i) + S(i), \quad i = 1, 2, \cdots, M$$

6. Two one-dimensional arrays, A and B, have a maximum of 18 elements each. N is a fixed point number not greater than 18. Compute

$$C = \sum_{k=1}^{N} A_k B_k$$

*7. A one-dimensional array named F contains at most 50 elements. Each of the first M elements, except

the first and Mth, is to be replaced by

$$F_i = \frac{F_{i-1} + F_i + F_{i+1}}{3}$$

Each new element is to be used immediately in the following computation.

*8. A one-dimensional array named B contains 50 elements. Place the largest of these elements in BIGB and place the element number of BIGB in NBIGB.

9. Two one-dimensional arrays named X and Y contain 50 elements each. A variable named XS is known to be equal to one of the elements in X. If $XS = X_i$, place Y_i in YS.

*10. Two one-dimensional arrays named X and Y contain 50 elements each. The elements in the X array form a monotonic increasing sequence, that is, $X_{i+1} > X_i$, $i = 1, 2, \cdots, 49$. If $XT < X_1$ or $XT > X_{50}$, transfer to statement 4190. If $XT = X_i$ for any i, place Y_i in YT. Otherwise, find two elements of the X array such that $X_{i-1} < XT < X_i$ and compute YT from

$$YT = Y_{i-1} + \frac{Y_i - Y_{i-1}}{X_i - X_{i-1}}(XT - X_{i-1})$$

11. Two one-dimensional arrays named X and Y contain 50 elements each. The Y array is expected to have exactly one *local maximum*, that is, three elements such that

$$Y_{i-1} < Y_i > Y_{i+1}$$

If there is no local maximum, transfer to statement 701; if there is more than one, transfer to statement 709; if there is exactly one, place X_i in XLOC and the value of i in LOC and transfer to statement 800.

*12. A two-dimensional array A contains 15 rows and 15 columns. A one-dimensional array X contains 15 elements. Compute the 15 elements of a one-dimensional array B according to

$$B_i = \sum_{j=1}^{15} A_{ij}X_j, \quad i = 1, 2, \cdots, 15$$

13. Three two-dimensional arrays, A, B, and C, have 15 rows and 15 columns each. Compute the elements of C according to

$$C_{ij} = \sum_{k=1}^{15} A_{ik}B_{kj}, \quad i, j = 1, 2, \cdots, 15$$

*14. A two-dimensional array, RST, has 20 rows and 20 columns. Compute the product of the main diagonal elements of RST and store it in DPROD. A main diagonal element is one with the same row and column number.

*15. The formula

$$Y = 41.926 \sqrt{1 + X^3} + X^{1/3}e^X$$

is to be evaluated for

$$X = 1.00, 1.01, 1.02, \cdots, 3.00$$

Each X, Y pair is to be punched on a card. Write a program using a DO loop to do this.

16. The formula

$$Z = \frac{e^{AX} - e^{-AX}}{2} \sin(X + B) + A \log \frac{B + X}{2}$$

is to be evaluated for all combinations of

$$X: \quad 1.0(0.1)2.0$$
$$A: \quad 0.10(0.05)0.80$$
$$B: \quad 1.0(1.0)10.0$$

where X: 1.00(0.1)2.00 means X = 1.0, 1.1, 1.2, $\cdots$, 2.0, etc. For each combination of X, A, and B (there are 1650 combinations) a card containing X, A, B, and Z is to be punched. Write a program containing three nested DO statements to do this.

17. In a certain problem Y is given as an empirical step function of X, according to a set of formulas such as

$$\text{if } X \leq A_1, \quad Y = Y_1$$
$$A_1 < X \leq A_2, \quad Y = Y_2$$
$$A_2 < X \leq A_3, \quad Y = Y_3$$
$$\cdots \cdots \cdots \cdots \cdots$$
$$A_{20} < X, \quad Y = Y_{21}$$

Set up appropriate arrays and a DO loop to find Y when X is given.

18. A solution to the following specialized system of equations is to be found:

$$A_{11}X_1 = b_1$$
$$A_{21}X_1 + A_{22}X_2 = b_2$$
$$A_{31}X_1 + A_{32}X_2 + A_{33}X_3 = b_3$$
$$\cdots \cdots \cdots \cdots \cdots \cdots \cdots \cdots \cdots$$
$$A_{n1}X_1 + A_{n2}X_2 + A_{n3}X_3 + \cdots + A_{nn}X_n = b_n$$

Such a system is easily solved, of course, by solving for X_1, substituting into equation 2, and so on. The difficulty, from the standpoint of computer solution, is that if a two-dimensional array is set up for the coefficients nearly half the storage locations will not be used—which pointlessly restricts the size of system that can be solved. Devise a method of storing the coefficients in a *one*-dimensional array and write a program to find the unknowns. Assume that it must be possible to handle 30 equations in 30 unknowns and include the necessary DIMENSION statement in the program.

7. FURTHER INFORMATION ON INPUT AND OUTPUT STATEMENTS*

7.1 Review

In Chapter 3 we discussed the input and output operations, which require the programmer to provide four categories of information.

1. The selection of an input or output device, which is handled by using the appropriate statement.

2. The variables to receive new input values or to be sent to an output device, as specified by the list of variables in the statement.

3. The order in which the values are to be transmitted, which is governed by the order in which the variables are named in the list.

4. The format in which the data appears, for input, or is to be written, for output, which is specified by a FORMAT statement referenced by the input or output statement.

Input and output operations in the larger FORTRAN systems provide the flexibility to handle effectively a wide variety of applications. In this chapter we investigate some of the features that provide convenience of operation and programming.

* Very little of the material in this chapter applies to the smaller FORTRAN systems, and the parts that do have been discussed previously. The user of such a system will miss no new applicable information if this chapter is passed over. Nevertheless, a quick reading, to get an idea of the full scope of the FORTRAN language, is recommended.

7.2 The List of an Input or Output Statement

The lists that we have seen so far are of the simplest type (and the most commonly used). We have named the variables explicitly in the order in which they are to be transmitted. In a statement such as

READ 169, A, X, F (1), F (2), M16

where 169 is the statement number of a FORMAT statement, the list consists of the names of the five variables. The first field on the card would be used as the new value of A, the second as X, etc., with the fields being defined by the FORMAT statement.

The important thing to keep in mind is the scanning process by which the card field, the variable name, and the field specification in the FORMAT statement are matched up. In a simple list everything starts at the left; successive items are taken in sequence. The first data field goes with the first variable name and the first field specification, and so on. This is the basic pattern, but we shall see that the various flexibilities permitted make the picture more complicated (in order to make the language more powerful).

The first additional list feature is a very useful one and one that does not complicate the scanning process: it is permissible to use fixed point variables in a list as subscripts elsewhere in the same list. There are two restrictions, however.

1. When this is done with input, any variable used as a subscript must appear in the list as an input variable *before* it appears as a subscript. "Before" means in the sense of the scanning process; in fact, it always means "to the left."

2. A left parenthesis (other than a subscripting parenthesis) must appear between the list variable appearance and the subscript appearance. For a "simple" list this requires enclosing the subscripted variable in parentheses.

One useful way to take advantage of this flexibility is in reading elements of an array that appear in the deck in random order. Suppose, for instance, that the elements of a two-dimensional array are punched one-to-a-card, with the row and column number of each element punched on the card with it, in the order I, J, A(I, J). The reading might be done with the statements

READ 400, I, J, (A(I, J))
400 FORMAT (I2, I2, E14.7)

The parentheses around A(I, J) are those required by Rule 2. Now, as each element is read, the information on the card is used immediately to specify where to store the element (i.e., to establish which element it is).

When entire arrays or parts of arrays are to be transmitted, it is often not necessary to name each element explicitly. To transmit an entire array, it is necessary only to name the array in a list without any subscripts. The name of the array must, of course, appear elsewhere in the program in a DIMENSION statement, but in the list it need not carry any subscripting information. The elements ordinarily have the same field specification; this one field specification may be given by itself in the FORMAT statement. We can, for instance, write

PRINT 21, A
21 FORMAT (E20.7)

where A is an array of any size. This is based on an additional feature of the scanning of the FORMAT statement: whenever the closing parenthesis of a FORMAT statement is reached, scanning starts again from the beginning (in this case). In this example there is obviously only one field specification, which is the most elementary example of this situation: the one field specification is simply used over and over, until all variables have been transmitted.

Whenever an entire array is moved this way, the elements are transmitted in the "natural order" mentioned on p. 33: the sequence is such that the first subscript varies most rapidly and the last varies least rapidly.

When only some of the elements of an array are to be transferred, or when the "natural order" is not desired, it is often still possible to avoid naming each element explicitly. They can instead be specified in the list in a way that parallels a DO loop, although it is not literally a DO loop. For instance, the statements

READ 200, (A(1, J),   J = 1, 10)
200 FORMAT (10F7.0)

would call for ten numbers to be read from a card and stored as the first ten elements of the first row of the array named A. The same ten numbers would be stored as the first ten elements of the first *column* of A by

READ 200, (A(I, 1),   I = 1, 10)

We see that the indexed variable (or variables), along with the indexing information, must be enclosed in parentheses.

Just as it is possible to have nests of DO's, it is possible to have nests of a maximum of three indexed variables in a list. Suppose, for example, that we want to print 60 numbers, taking the first 12 as the first 12 elements of the first row of RESULT, the next 12 as the first 12 elements of the *third* row of RESULT, the next 12 as the first 12 in the *fifth* row, etc. This can be done with:

PRINT 91, ((RESULT(I,J),J = 1,12),I = 1,9,2)
91 FORMAT (E20.7)

In a certain sense, this list may be thought of as equivalent to the DO nest:

DO   462   I = 1, 9, 2
DO   462   J = 1, 12
462 RESULT(I, J)

In this analogy, statement 462 is to be understood in the sense that "the next number printed is to be RESULT(I, J)." Thus it is seen that the idea of "inner" and "outer" DO's carries over to inner and outer list indexing.

We see here that the scanning of a list can become considerably more complicated than it is in a simple list, which names each variable explicitly. Still, the sequence in which numbers are transferred is completely specified. We need to note how list scanning keeps in step with FORMAT statement scanning: as each new variable name is picked up from the list, another field specification is obtained from the FORMAT statement. The indexing of the list and the FORMAT statement variations discussed below make the picture more complex but do not change the basic idea of simultaneous scanning of the list and the field specifications.

Indexing may be set up to use fixed point variables earlier in the list as indexing parameters. When this is done, the parentheses that must enclose the indexed variable(s) and the indexing information will satisfy Rule 2 on p. 46. When the application demands it, list indexing can be used to handle input and output operations in quite complex ways. Such situations are uncommon, however, in the work of a nonprofessional programmer, and we shall not pursue the subject further.

7.3 The FORMAT Statement

It is the business of the FORMAT statement to describe how the information is arranged, on input, or is to be arranged, on output. To each number transmitted, there must correspond a field specification which lists the kind of information the field contains and what it "looks like" (or will look like, for output). The subject may conveniently be described under two headings: (1) what each of the types of field specifications does and (2) how the field specifications may be arranged in the FORMAT statement, in keeping with the scanning process.

We shall discuss four types of field specifications. (Some FORTRAN systems permit others, but they would seldom be used by a nonprofessional programmer.) In each case a complete field specification consists of the following:

1. A letter (I, F, E, or H) to designate the type of information and something about how it is to be handled.

2. A number to designate how many card columns or printer spaces are involved.

The E and F field specifications require a second number to prescribe decimal point handling.

To save repetition, we may note some facts that apply to each of the field specifications I, F, and E.

On *input* a sign, if any, must be the first non-blank character of the field. The use of a plus sign is always optional; if no sign appears, the number is taken to be positive. Embedded blanks are taken to be zeros.

On *output* the number will appear at the right of the assigned field if more characters are specified for the field than there are characters in the number. If too few characters are specified, the sign and high-order digits will be lost and no indication given. Plus signs are not punched or printed.

In all four kinds it is permissible to specify that the same field specification applies to several successive fields by writing a *repetition number* in front of the field specification.

Field Specification I (Integer)

This is of the form Iw. I specifies conversion between an internal fixed point integer and an external decimal integer. The total number of characters in the field, including sign and any blanks, is w. For most practical purposes, the integer must be smaller than 32,768. Decimal points are not permitted.

Field Specification F (External Fixed Point)

This is of the form $Fw.d$. The F indicates conversion between an internal floating point number and an external number written without an exponent. The total number of characters in the field, including sign, decimal point, and any blanks, is w. The number of decimal places after the (assumed) decimal point is d.

On *input* the use of an actual decimal point is optional: if one is supplied, it overrides d. Shown below are some sample data fields and the numbers to which they would be converted if read under control of F10.6.

Data Field	Converted Internal Number
+12345678	+12.345678
1234.5678	+1234.5678
−1.2345678	−1.2345678
.012345678	+.01234567
−1.2	−1.2
+1234567	+1.234567
123	+.000123

On *output* there will be d places to the right of the decimal point. For example, consider the floating point numbers 1.2345678, 12.345678, and −123.45678. With the field specification 3F11.5, they would print as

1.23457   12.34568   -123.45678

Note that each number has been rounded to five decimal places and that each occupies a total of 11 spaces. With the field specification 3F8.2 they would appear as

1.23   12.35   -123.46

If the field specification F8.5 were used, there would be trouble because there would not be enough space to contain the numbers. The result would be

1.2345712.3456823.45678

This illustrates that when using the F field specification it is essential to know the maximum sizes of all numbers, a problem that is avoided when the E field specification is used.

Field Specification E (Floating Point)

This is of the form E$w.d$. E specifies conversion between an internal floating point number and an external number written with an exponent. The total number of characters in the field in external medium is w, including sign, decimal point, exponent, and any blanks. The number of decimal places after the decimal point (not counting the exponent) is d.

On *input* the use of an actual decimal point is optional; if one is supplied, it overrides d. The exponent part of the field is of the general form E$\pm ee$, the same as in a floating point constant in a statement. However, several short cuts are permitted to simplify card punching.

A positive exponent may appear with the + omitted or replaced with a blank, that is, in the form E ee or Eee. If the first digit of the exponent is zero, it may be omitted. If the exponent is written with a sign, the E may be omitted. Thus the following are all permissible (and equivalent) forms for the exponent *plus 2:* E+02, E 02, E02, E+2, E2, +02, +2.

For example, observe that the following data fields convert to the same internal number if read in under the control of E14.7 (remember that an

actual decimal point overrides d in the field specification):

+12345678E03   1234.5678E0
12345678.E$-$4   +0.12345678+4

On *output* the number will normally appear in the form $\pm 0.nn \cdots \text{E} \pm ee$ (except that plus signs are replaced with blanks), where the number of places after the decimal point is specified by d.

A *scale factor* may be used by writing the field specification in the form sPnE$w.d$, where s is the scale factor, P stands for "place" or "point," and n is the repetition number. The effect of the scale factor is to move the decimal point s places to the right and decrease the exponent by s.

A scale factor has no effect on input with an E field specification. It has an effect on both input and output with an F field specification, but such usage is not common. When a scale factor is used, it applies to all subsequent E and F field specifications in the same FORMAT statement, as the scanning continues, until another scale factor is encountered. This means that if a scale factor is to apply to only one field specification, the one following it must have a scale factor of zero.

For an example, suppose there are three numbers which under control of 3E17.8 would print as shown in the first line of Figure 7.1. The same numbers printed under control of 3E12.3 would print as shown in the second line. Printed under control of 1P3E11.4, the numbers would appear as shown in the third line. Notice that by allowing only the minimum number of spaces we have crowded the printing, making it difficult to read.

For routine printing of floating point results, the most common field specification is probably 1PE20.7. This prints the decimal point between the first and second digits, prints all the significant figures available, and provides plenty of space for easy reading.

Field Specification H (Hollerith)

This is of the form wH. The w characters immediately following the letter H are printed or

0.12345678E 03   -0.55555555E 00   0.87654321E-05

0.123E 03   -0.556E 00   0.877E-05

1.2346E 02-5.5556E-01 8.7654E-06

Figure 7.1. Three ways of printing the same numbers, showing the effect of different FORMAT statements.

punched in the position indicated by the position of the Hollerith field specification in the FORMAT statement. (The term is based on the work of Dr. Herman Hollerith, who invented the method of representing alphabetic characters on a punched card.) The Hollerith field specification is different from the others in that it does not go with a variable named in the list. Instead, it calls for the output of the text *itself*. Any character available in the computer system may be used, including the "character" *blank*. This is the only case in which a blank in a statement is not simply ignored. No indication of the presence of Hollerith text is required in the list of the output statement that refers to the FORMAT statement containing the text. Whenever a Hollerith field specification is encountered in the scanning of a FORMAT statement, the text following is written out and scanning continues without any variable from the list having been transmitted. It is possible to print a line or punch a card consisting entirely of Hollerith text by putting nothing but Hollerith text in the FORMAT statement and giving no list with the output statement.

One of the most frequent applications of the Hollerith field specification is in controlling the spacing of the lines of printing. The first character of the line printed with a PRINT statement is actually not printed but is instead used to control spacing of the printer carriage. If the carriage control character is a blank, the normal single spacing occurs before the line is printed. If the carriage control character is zero, double spacing occurs before printing. If the character is 1, the paper spaces to the top of the next page before printing. (More than this can be done, in fact, but the additional features are seldom used by the nonprofessional programmer.) The same considerations apply when a tape written with the WRITE OUTPUT TAPE statement (see below) is printed, if the appropriate switch on the off-line printer is set to Program Control.

7.4 Additional FORMAT Statement Features

Just as it is possible to repeat a field specification by writing a repetition number in front of it, it is also possible to repeat a *group* of field specifications. The group is enclosed in parentheses,

and the desired number of repetitions is written in before it. For instance, suppose that eight fields on a card are alternately described by I2 and F10.0. We can write 4(I2, F10.0) to get the desired action. This is *not* the same as 4I2, 4F10.0, which would describe a card with four I2 fields, then four F10.0 fields, rather than the intended alternation. Only one such level of grouping is permitted, that is, parentheses within parentheses are not permitted.

When the list of an input or output statement is used to transmit more than one *record* (card or line), with the different records having different formats, a slash (/) is used to separate the format specifications for the different records. For example, suppose that two cards are to be read with a single READ statement; the first card has only a four-digit integer and the second has six floating point numbers. We could write

$$\text{FORMAT (I4/6E14.0)}$$

It is possible to specify a special format for the first one or more records and a different format from the first group for all subsequent records. This is done by enclosing the last record specifications in parentheses. For instance, if the first card of a deck has an integer and a floating point number and all following contain two integers and a floating point number, we could write

$$\text{FORMAT (I4, E14.0/(2I4, E14.0))}$$

A slash always indicates the end of one record and the beginning of a new one. The closing parenthesis of the FORMAT statement marks the end of a record. The skipping of entire records (on the printer, usually) is called for by writing successive slashes. Note that the skipping of n records is called for by $n + 1$ successive slashes.

We are now able to summarize the scanning process. The list in the input or output statement specifies the variables to be transmitted and their sequence (taking into account any indexing). The associated FORMAT statement specifies the length and format of each field, as well as the length of each record if there is more than one. As the variables in the list are transmitted, the FORMAT statement is scanned from left to right to find the field specification associated with each variable. The scanning of course takes into account any repetition of field specification or of groups of them. Whenever Hollerith field specifications are encountered in scanning the FORMAT statement, they are handled in the proper place without the transmission of variables from the list. The transmission of variables is ended only when all named in the list have been moved, but any remaining Hollerith field specifications will be dealt with even after the transmission of the last variable named in the list. If variables remain to be transmitted when the last field specification in the FORMAT statement has been used, scanning begins again with the first field specification in the last set of parentheses in the FORMAT statement.

A few examples may help to clarify some of these ideas. Suppose that we wish to read a deck of cards containing elements of a one-dimensional array named DATA. The first card contains only the value of a number N, punched in columns 1–2, which specifies how many cards there are in the rest of the deck. Each remaining card contains an element number in 1–2 and the value of the element in 3–15, in a form for reading with E13.0. The deck can be read and each element stored in the proper location with the following two statements:

    READ 69, N, (K, (DATA(K)), I = 1, N)
    69 FORMAT (I2/(I2, E13.0))

In the READ statement the outer set of parentheses indicates variables controlled by list indexing, which in this case is used simply to read the proper number of cards. The parentheses around DATA(K) are those required by Rule 2 on p. 46. In the FORMAT statement the slash says that the first card contains only the one integer. The parentheses around I2, E13.0 will cause repeated scanning of those two field specifications.

For a second example suppose that an output page is to be printed with a page heading and column identifications as shown in Figure 7.2. Note that there are two blank lines between the heading and the body. The "X =" and "Y =" are obtained with a FORMAT statement containing suitable Hollerith text (as is the heading). The X and Y values are the elements of two one-dimensional arrays of six elements each. The statements to do all this are shown in Figure 7.3.

We have here an example of a PRINT statement without a list. The FORMAT statement for printing the heading contains only Hollerith text and the three slashes to skip two lines, but no numeric field specifications. The second PRINT statement uses list indexing to specify the six elements of each array. The second FORMAT statement illustrates several features. The 3H X = causes the "X =" to be printed at the start of each line; note that no comma is required after a Hollerith field specification. The blank calls for single spacing. The X values will be printed under control of 1PE16.7. Recall that the "1P" will move the decimal point one place to the right and adjust the exponent accordingly. In 4H Y =, note that the two blanks are included in the count of the number of characters in the Hollerith field. This is necessary because otherwise the "Y =" would print next to the X value, with no space, and would produce a confusing report. The Y value is to be printed in the same way as the X value, with the decimal point shifted right one place; the "1P" is not required because once a scale factor is given it continues in effect for the rest of that FORMAT statement until another one is scanned. (On the other hand, writing the Y field specification with the "1P" would not hurt anything.)

ACCELERATION CALCULATION

```
X=    4.9143062E-02   Y=   -6.1243299E 05
X=    6.1462201E-02   Y=   -9.4016230E 05
X=    8.9001657E-02   Y=   -2.6033842E 06
X=    1.1297321E-01   Y=   -5.5610328E 07
X=    5.0163284E-01   Y=   -9.8632141E 07
X=    8.6489962E-01   Y=   -4.1126813E 08
```

Figure 7.2. Sample output produced by the program of Figure 7.3.

```
C FOR COMMENT
STATEMENT
NUMBER      Cont.                    FORTRAN STATEMENT                          72
1        5  6 7

        PRINT 400
  400   FØRMAT (25H ACCELERATIØN CALCULATIØN ///)
        PRINT 401, (X(I), Y(I), I = 1,6)
  401   FØRMAT (3H X= 1PE16.7, 4H  Y= E16.7)
```

Figure 7.3. Program segment to produce the output of Figure 7.2.

7.5 Magnetic Tape Operations

An important feature of all large computers is the availability of magnetic tape, which is used in two rather different ways.

The more common application is in speeding up input and output operations. Reading cards at a few hundred a minute is very slow compared with the internal arithmetic speed of a large computer and printing is little better. Therefore, except when the amount of input and output is very small, the usual procedure is to use magnetic tape to reduce the wasted computer time. This is done, in the case of input, by first taping the information on the cards with a separate card-to-tape converter that is not connected to the computer. While this is being done, the computer can be used for other work. When the problem is ready to be run, the magnetic tape is mounted on a tape unit that is connected to the computer, and the problem data is read in at about a hundred times the speed of card reading.

Similarly, problem results are written on magnetic tape rather than directly printed. When the problem is completed, the output tape is moved from the computer to a separate tape unit connected to a printer. The results are then printed while the computer is engaged in other work.

This perhaps sounds like more trouble than it is. In practice, the whole operation runs very smoothly, and the programmer ordinarily has nothing to do with the mechanics of the tape handling. The net result is a considerable increase in computer efficiency.

The other, less common use of magnetic tape provides intermediate storage for results during the solution of a problem. For instance, some problems involve very large arrays, which may be too big to fit in computer storage at one time. In such a case the intermediate results can be written on magnetic tape as they are computed and read back in when they are needed.

The two tape applications require two different kinds of statements because of the simpler way the tape can be read and written if it is to be used only by the computer than if it must be usable by other equipment also.

The READ INPUT TAPE statement is used to read a tape produced on the card-to-tape converter. It is handled just like a READ statement, with one minor exception: it is necessary to specify the number of the tape unit on which the reel of tape is mounted. This tape number is written before the FORMAT statement number. A typical statement would be

READ INPUT TAPE 2, 169, I, A, X1, SEG

The 2 specifies tape unit 2; in all other respects the statement is the same as a READ statement. The requirements of the FORMAT statement are the same, list indexing is the same, and the scanning process is the same.

The WRITE OUTPUT TAPE statement is similarly analogous to the PRINT statement. A typical statement would be

WRITE OUTPUT TAPE 3, 401,
         (X(I), Y(I), I = 1,6)

The choice of the tape unit is determined largely by the conventions established by the particular computer installation.

For operations with intermediate tapes, which are not involved with card reading or with printing, the READ TAPE and WRITE TAPE statements are used. These statements are different from other input and output statements because they do not require a FORMAT statement. A typical statement would be

WRITE TAPE 6, ARRAY

ARRAY is assumed to be large array; the name is written without subscripts, so that the entire array will be written. *The tape so written cannot be printed* because the data words are written just as they appear in computer storage, without conversion to a form suitable for printing. Its only meaningful function is to read it back into storage with a READ TAPE statement.

Three other statements are related to tape operations, although they do not themselves transmit information. BACKSPACE n, where n is the number of a tape unit, backs up the tape beyond one record. A record, in this case, means either the information corresponding to one card or printer line or all the information written by one WRITE TAPE statement. END FILE n puts a mark on the tape that will be recognized by the tape-to-printer converter as signifying the end of a printer run. The REWIND n statement returns the tape to its beginning. It may then be removed, if it is an input or output tape, or re-employed, if it is an intermediate tape. (Writing new information on a tape automatically erases what had been on it before.) All tapes should be rewound *before* use.

EXERCISES

*1. Four numbers are punched on a card; they are new values of floating point variables named BOS, EWR, PHL, and DCA. Each number is punched in eight columns, with a decimal point. Write READ and FORMAT statements to read the card.

2. Same as Exercise 1, except that there is no decimal point. The numbers are to be treated as if they had two decimal places, that is, two places to the right of an assumed decimal point.

3. Same as Exercise 1, except that each number occupies 14 columns and is punched with an exponent (and a decimal point).

*4. A card is punched in the following format.

Columns	Sample Format	Associated Variable Name
1–3	$\pm xx$	LGA
4–6	xxx	IDL
7–20	$\pm x.xxxxxxxE \pm ee$	BAL
21–34	$\pm x.xxxxxxxE \pm ee$	ATL

The small letters stand for any digits. Write statements to read such a card.

*5. DATA is a one-dimensional array of at most ten elements. A card is punched with a value of N in columns 1–2 and with one to ten elements of DATA in succeeding columns. The number of elements is given by the value of N. Each number is punched with a

decimal point but no exponent in seven columns. Write statements to read such a card.

6. Same as Exercise 5, except that the numbers are the *odd*-numbered elements of DATA; there are therefore five of them at most. N is the *element number* of the last one, not the total number of elements.

*7. M is a two-dimensional array of fixed point numbers, with three rows and four columns. A card is punched with the 12 elements of M, each integer taking three columns. Write statements to read such a card. In what order must the elements be punched to allow the simplest READ statement list?

8. L is a three-dimensional array, with maximum subscripts given in

DIMENSION L(2,2,3)

A card is punched with the 12 elements of L, each integer taking three columns. Write statements to read such a card. In what order must the elements be punched to allow the simplest READ statement list?

*9. The values of the variables A, B, X, and Z are to be printed on one line. A and B are to be printed without exponents, X and Z with. Twelve spaces should be allowed for A and B, and they should have four decimal places. Twenty spaces should be allowed for X and Z, and they should be printed in the normal form with eight decimal places. Write statements to do this.

10. Same as Exercise 9, except that a positive integer named K is to be printed in six spaces between A and B, and the decimal point is to be moved one place to the right in X and Z.

*11. A two-dimensional array named ABC consists of ten rows and four columns. Write a program to write the following on output tape 3. At the top of the page printed from the tape is the heading "MATRIX ABC." The elements are then printed in the normal row-and-column arrangement for a two-dimensional array using E20.8 field specifications. (*Hint.* Be sure that exactly four numbers are printed on each line.)

12. A one-dimensional array named CVG contains a maximum of 40 elements. The input tape on tape unit 2 was prepared from a deck consisting of one card per element. Each card contains the element number in columns 1–2 and the element itself in columns 3–12, punched with a decimal point but without an exponent. The cards are not assumed to be in correct order. It is not known how many cards there are, but the last card of the deck is blank, which will look like an element number of zero. Write a program to read the tape and place each value in the correct location in the array.

*13. A two-dimensional array PHX is named in the DIMENSION statement

DIMENSION PHX(10, 13)

The actual number of rows and columns is given by the values of the variables M and N, respectively. Write a program to punch out as many elements as there actually are in the array, in row order. Each element should be punched on a separate card, with its row and column numbers. Use I2 for the fixed point numbers and 1PE20.7 for the floating point.

14. The elements of a two-dimensional array U are to be viewed as the values of a function at the mesh-points of a square grid. Values of the function at some or all of these points are punched on a deck of cards. Each card contains values of the variables I, J, and U(I, J), where I and J are the row and column numbers of the element. Suitable field specifications are I2, I2, and F10.0. There are 20 rows and 20 columns in the array, but there are ordinarily fewer than 400 data cards; the end of the deck is signaled by a card with a dummy row number of 99. Write a program to read the data cards, then carry out the following procedure. Each of the *interior* points of the array is to be replaced by

$$U_{ij} = \frac{U_{i-1,j} + U_{i+1,j} + U_{i,j-1} + U_{i,j+1}}{4}$$

As each new interior point is computed, form the absolute value of the difference between the new and old values of U; form the sum of all of these *residues*. The computation of a new value of U at all interior points and the computation of the sum of the residues is called a *sweep* of the grid. Continue sweeping the grid until the sum of the residues on one sweep is less than 0.01. Then punch out the entire array, with each element on a separate card identified by row and column number. (One method of iterative solution of Laplace's equation.)

A block diagram is recommended.

8. FUNCTIONS AND SPECIFICATION STATEMENTS *

8.1 Introduction

The various functions of the system greatly increase the power and flexibility of FORTRAN. We have so far discussed only those supplied with the system, which require no effort from the programmer beyond writing the proper name where the function value is desired. After reviewing these functions briefly, we may go on to consider the three other types that can be set up by the programmer to do whatever he wishes and the two statements that are used in conjunction with them.

Most FORTRAN systems provide in the neighborhood of three dozen functions to compute such things as trigonometric functions, logarithms, and absolute values. The exact list depends not only on the computer and the version of FORTRAN used but on the particular installation. Most installations provide special-purpose functions to meet their individual needs. Some provide a common logarithm *and* a natural logarithm, even though one can easily be obtained from the other, because both are frequently needed. An installation doing orbit calculations might have a special function to compute air density as a function of altitude. Each programmer must have an up-to-date list of the functions available at his installation, along with a precise write-up that gives such information as accuracy, speed, whether angles are in degrees or radians, etc.

In order to use these functions, it is necessary only to write their names where they are needed, entering the desired expression(s) for the argument(s). (Many permit several arguments, such as the function that finds the smallest of the values of the arguments listed.) The names of these functions are all established in advance, and the programmer must write them exactly as specified. Although the programmer has no control over their naming, we may note that the names are always four to seven characters in length, always end in F, and always begin with a letter, which is X if and only if the value of the function is fixed point.

The functions available as a part of the system are actually of two different types, depending on the mechanics of their insertion in the object program. The *open* functions require only a few machine instructions; these instructions are inserted into the object program every time the function is used. The *closed* functions are in general considerably longer; they are inserted into the object program in one place only, and the object program transfers to that one place whenever it is needed. This distinction is ordinarily of no importance to the nonprofessional programmer.

---

* Most of the material in this chapter does not apply to the smaller FORTRAN systems, and the parts that do apply have been covered in preceding chapters.

8.2 Arithmetic Statement Functions

It often happens that a programmer will find some relatively simple computation recurring through his program, making it desirable to be able to set up a function to carry out the computation. This function would be needed only in the one program, so that there would be no point to setting up a new function for the purpose—which is a bit of work. Instead, a function can be defined for the purpose of the one program and then used wherever desired in that program. It has no effect on any other program.

An arithmetic statement function is *defined* by writing a statement of the form $a = b$, where a is the name of the function and b is an expression. The name, which is invented by the programmer, must conform to the same rules as the functions supplied with the system: it must be four to seven characters in length, the last letter must be F, and the first must be a letter, which is X if and only if the value of the function is fixed point. It must not, of course, be the same as the name of any supplied function. The name of the function is followed by parentheses enclosing the argument(s), which are separated by commas if there is more than one. The arguments *in the definition* may not be subscripted.

The right-hand side of the definition statement may be any expression not involving subscripted variables. It may use variables not specified as arguments and it may use other functions (except itself!). All function definitions must appear before the first executable statement of the program.

This is only the *definition* of the function; it does not cause computation to take place. The variable names used as arguments are only dummies; they may be the same as variable names appearing elsewhere in the program. The argument names are unimportant, except as they specify fixed or floating point.

An arithmetic statement function is *used* by writing its name wherever the function value is desired and adding any appropriate expressions for arguments. The values of these expressions will be substituted into the program segment established by the definition and the value of the function computed. These actual arguments may be subscripted if desired.

As an illustration, suppose that in a certain program it is frequently necessary to compute one of the roots of the quadratic equation $aX^2 + bX +$

$c = 0$, given values of a, b, and c. A function can be defined to carry out this computation, for instance, by writing

$$\mathrm{ROOTF}(A, B, C)$$
$$= (-B + \mathrm{SQRTF}(B**2 - 4.*A*C))/(2.*A)$$

This *defines* the function; the compiler will produce a sequence of instructions in the object program to compute the value of the function, given three values to use in the computation.

Suppose now that it is desired to use this function, with 16.9 for a, $R-S$ for b, and $T+6.9$ for c; the value of the function (root) is to be added to the cosine of X and the sum stored as the new value of ANS. All this can be done with the statement

$$\mathrm{ANS} = \mathrm{ROOTF}(16.9, R-S, T+6.9) + \mathrm{COSF}(X)$$

Suppose that later in the program it is necessary to compute the function with DATA(I) for a, DATA(I+1) for b, and 0.087 for c; the function value is to be cubed and stored as the value of TEMP:

$$\mathrm{TEMP}$$
$$= \mathrm{ROOTF}(\mathrm{DATA}(I), \mathrm{DATA}(I + 1), 0.087)**3$$

It must be emphasized that the variables A, B, and C in the function definition have no relation to any variables of the same name elsewhere in the program. To illustrate, suppose that the value of the root is needed for an equation

$$22.97X^2 + AX + B = 0$$

where A and B are simply variables in the program. The root may be found by writing

$$\mathrm{VAL} = \mathrm{ROOTF}(22.97, A, B)$$

The A and B that appear here in the *use* of the function are completely unrelated to the A and B in the *definition* of the function. In summary, the variables in the definition are simply dummies that establish how the expression values in the use should be substituted into the object program segment set up from the definition.

8.3 Subprograms

Useful as an arithmetic statement function often is, it does have two rather serious restrictions: the definition is limited to one statement and it can compute only one value. The FUNCTION subprogram removes the first restriction and the SUBROUTINE removes both of them.

This is only half the story, however, and actually the less important half. The outstanding feature of these two types of functions is that they are *subprograms;* they can be compiled independently of the main program of which they are a part. Their variable names are completely independent of the variable names in the main program and in other subprograms. They may have their own DIMENSION statements (and the other specification statements described below). In short, FUNCTION and SUBROUTINE subprograms can be completely independent of the main program—yet it is quite easy to set up "communication" between the main program and the subprograms. This means that a large program can be divided into parts that can be compiled individually, making it possible to correct errors in one subprogram without recompiling the entire program.

Whether these subprograms are viewed as powerful extensions of the arithmetic statement function idea or as a way to segment a program, they are a most valuable part of the language.

As with the arithmetic statement function, we must distinguish carefully between the definition and the use. The computation of a FUNCTION subprogram is *defined* by writing the necessary statements in a segment, writing the word FUNCTION and the name of the function before the segment, and writing the word END after them. The name may have one to six characters, the first of which must be alphabetic; the first character must be I, J, K, L, M, or N if and only if the value of the function is fixed point; the last character must *not* be F if the name is more than three characters long. (Note the difference in naming.) The name must appear at least once in the subprogram as a variable on the left-hand side of an arithmetic statement or in the list of an input statement. The name of the subprogram is followed by parentheses enclosing the argument(s), which are separated by commas if there is more than one.

As before, the arguments in the subprogram definition are only dummy variables. The arguments in the function name must be distinct nonsubscripted variables or array names. Within the subprogram itself, however, subscripted variables may be used freely. The subprogram must contain at least one RETURN statement, for reasons that we shall see immediately below.

To *use* the FUNCTION subprogram, it is necessary only to write the name of the function with suitable expressions for arguments. The mechanics of the operation of the object program are as follows. The FUNCTION subprogram is compiled as a set of machine instructions in one place in storage. Wherever the name of the subprogram appears in the source program a transfer to the subprogram is set up in the object program. When the computations of the subprogram have been completed, a transfer is made back to the section of the program that brought the subprogram into action. The RETURN statement(s) in the subprogram in effect tells the compiler at what point to go back to the main program. (This is actually quite similar to the way an arithmetic statement function is set up, except in that case there can only be one statement and so there is no question when to return.)

As a simple example of the use of a FUNCTION subprogram, suppose that in a certain program it is frequently necessary to compute the function

```
C FOR COMMENT
STATEMENT
 NUMBER   Cont.
1     5   6 7              FORTRAN STATEMENT                    72
            FUNCTION Y(X)
            IF(X - 2.1) 40, 40, 30
     40     Y = 0.5*X + 0.95
            RETURN
     30     Y = 0.7*X + 0.53
            RETURN
            END
```

Figure 8.1. An example of a FUNCTION subprogram.

```
C FOR COMMENT
STATEMENT                                      FORTRAN STATEMENT
NUMBER                                                                                    72
1        5 6 7

         FUNCTION DIAGPR (A, N)
         DIMENSION A (10, 10)
         DIAGPR = A (1, 1)
         DO 69 I = 2, N
   69    DIAGPR = DIAGPR * A (I, I)
         RETURN
         END
```

Figure 8.2. Another example of a FUNCTION subprogram.

shown on p. 25. The function can be defined with the statements in Figure 8.1, where the name Y has been given to the function.

If we now want to compute this function for an argument equal to GRS − 6.8 and divide the result by 12.99 to get the value of EWR, we can write

$$EWR = Y(GRS - 6.8)/12.99$$

To get the square root of this function of the square root of one plus RHO, we can write

$$PDX = SQRTF(Y(SQRTF(1. + RHO)))$$

A FUNCTION subprogram may have many arguments, including arrays. For example, suppose that it is necessary to find the product of the main diagonal elements (those having the same row and column numbers) of square arrays. The arrays from which this product is computed must have been mentioned in a DIMENSION statement in the program that uses the subprogram, as always, and all the arrays must have the same dimensions. The array names in the FUNCTION name and subprogram will be dummies, but the dummy array names must still be mentioned in a DIMENSION statement in the subprogram. Suppose that the arrays in question are all ten by ten maximum but that the *actual* arrays can be smaller, with the actual size being given by the value of a fixed point variable. The subprogram could be as shown in Figure 8.2.

Now, if we want the product of the main diagonal elements of an array named DATA, in which the actual size is given by the value of LAST, we could write

$$DET = DIAGPR(DATA, LAST)$$

To find the square of the product of the main diagonal elements of an array named X, in which the actual number of rows and columns is given by the value of JACK, we could write

$$EIG = DIAGPR(X, JACK)**2$$

A FUNCTION subprogram is seen to be quite similar to an arithmetic statement function, except that it can use many statements instead of just one and it can use any of the FORTRAN statements instead of just an arithmetic statement. A subprogram can use other subprograms except itself and any that uses itself. We shall consider the independent compilation aspect of a FUNCTION subprogram after discussing the SUBROUTINE subprogram.

The basics of the SUBROUTINE subprogram are quite similar to the FUNCTION subprogram, with three differences:

1. A SUBROUTINE may have many outputs instead of the one to which a FUNCTION is restricted.

2. Because of this, a SUBROUTINE cannot be used simply by writing its name. Instead, we write a CALL statement to bring it into action; this specifies the arguments and stores all of the output values.

3. Since the output of a SUBROUTINE may be a combination of fixed and floating point numbers, the first letter of the name is not required to designate fixed or floating point. The naming is otherwise the same.

In all other respects the two types of subprograms are entirely analogous. The essential features of the SUBROUTINE program are illustrated in the following example. Suppose that in a certain program it is frequently necessary to find the largest element (in absolute value) in a specified

```
          C FOR COMMENT
STATEMENT
NUMBER          FORTRAN STATEMENT
1        5 6 7                                                          72
        SUBROUTINE LARGE (ARRAY, I, BIG, J)
        DIMENSION ARRAY(10, 10)
        BIG = ABSF (ARRAY (I, 1))
        J = 1
        DO 69 K = 2, 10
        IF (ABSF (ARRAY (I, K)) - BIG) 69, 69, 70
   70   BIG = ABSF (ARRAY (I, K))
        J = K
   69   CONTINUE
        RETURN
        END
```

Figure 8.3. An example of a SUBROUTINE subprogram.

row of a ten by ten array. The input to the SUB-ROUTINE is therefore the array name and the row number. The output will be the absolute value of the largest element in that row and its column number. The SUBROUTINE could be as shown in Figure 8.3.

Now suppose that the largest element in the third row of a ten by ten array named ZETA is needed. The absolute value of the element is to be called DIVIS and the column number is to be called NCOL. We write the statement

CALL LARGE (ZETA, 3, DIVIS, NCOL)

This brings the subprogram into operation, stores the values of DIVIS and NCOL found by the subprogram, and returns to the statement following the CALL. If, later, it is necessary to find the largest element in row M + 2 of an array named DETAIL, storing its absolute value as SIZE and the column number as KWHICH, we can write

CALL LARGE(DETAIL, M + 2,

SIZE, KWHICH)

To emphasize the independence of the variable names between the main program and any subprograms, we may note that it would be possible to write the statement

CALL LARGE(ARRAY, I, BIG, J)

If this is done, all of the variables here must still be defined *in the calling program.* The name I in the calling program and the name I in the sub-program are unrelated. And this must logically be so: the name I in the subprogram tells what to do with a value from the calling program, whereas the name I in the calling program must specify a number that has previously been computed by the calling program.

8.4 The EQUIVALENCE and COMMON Statements

These two nonexecutable statements make possible certain conveniences in the naming of variables and the assignment of storage locations to them.

The EQUIVALENCE statement causes two or more variable names to be assigned to the same storage location, which is useful in two rather different ways.

In one usage the EQUIVALENCE statement allows the programmer to define two or more variable names as meaning the same thing. It might be that after writing a long program the programmer will realize that he has inadvertently changed variable names and that X, X1, and RST6 should refer to the same variable. Rather than going back and changing the variable names in the program, a time-consuming and error-prone process, he can write

EQUIVALENCE (X, X1, RST6)

and the mistake is corrected.

The other application is in making use of the same storage location to contain two or more variables that are never needed at the same time. Suppose that in the initial READ statement of a program the variable I27 appears but is never used after that. During the program, a DO parameter NP1 is established but only for that loop. Later, the variable JJM2 is applied to a similar purpose. At the end, the variable NEXT1 is used on the final PRINT statement. As it stands, four storage locations will be allocated to these variables, which is pointless since their usage never overlaps. If the programmer is short of storage space, he can assign all four variables to one location by writing

EQUIVALENCE (I27, NP1, JJM2, NEXT1)

The same thing could, of course, be accomplished by changing the variable names, but using an EQUIVALENCE is obviously simpler.

These two applications of EQUIVALENCE differ only in viewpoint; the statement and its treatment by the compiler are the same in either case.

One EQUIVALENCE statement can establish equivalence between any number of sets of variables. For instance, if A and B are to be made equivalent, as are X and Y, we can write

EQUIVALENCE (A, B), (X, Y)

The statement may also establish equivalences among arrays, but the subject is slightly involved and varies in different versions of FORTRAN. It is of little concern to the nonprofessional programmer; we refer the interested reader to the appropriate manuals and leave the matter.

The COMMON statement. It has been stated that each subprogram has its own variable names: the name X in the main program is not necessarily taken to be the same as the name X in a subprogram. However, if the programmer wishes them to mean the same, he can write the statement

COMMON (X)

in *both* places. The statement does considerably more, actually. Suppose, for instance, that we have the following statements:

Main program: COMMON (X, Y, I)
Subprogram: COMMON (A, B, J)

Then X and A are assigned to the same memory location, as are Y and B, and I and J. This not only saves storage locations but also provides a way to establish correspondence between variables in a main program and in subprograms, without actually naming them as arguments in the definitions.

8.5 Segmenting a Program

There are several reasons why it is often convenient to be able to break a program up into segments that can be compiled independently if desired. One has been mentioned above: correcting a few errors in one section of a large program requires re-compilation of the entire program, which is obviously wasteful. It is clearly an advantage to be able to compile only the part that contains the error. It is also valuable to be able to write a program in segments when several people are to work on the same job. Problems arise if each person's work must be regarded as a part of one main program: variable names must be coordinated, no one can compile his part until the entire program is finished, etc. A third value of program segmentation is that commonly used subprograms can easily be incorporated into other programs. All of these are met by proper use of subprograms, especially SUBROUTINE subprograms, and the COMMON statement.

One fairly common practice is to break a program into segments, rather arbitrarily, just to get the advantage of being able to recompile small parts independently. This practice is common partly because the segmentation can be done in an almost mechanical fashion.

The program is written as a short main program and a series of fairly short SUBROUTINE subprograms, using the same variable names in all. The subprogram names in the SUBROUTINE and CALL statements are written with *no arguments*. After the program is completed, one long COMMON statement is written which contains the names of all variables appearing anywhere in the program. This statement is duplicated (with a card reproducer, preferably) and included in the main program and all subprograms. In effect, the program is written in almost the same form as if it were one big program, except that it is segmented at logical dividing points into subroutines, and COMMON statements are included. The additional effort in writing the program is trivial, but now the various subprograms can be recompiled separately.

The practice is strongly recommended.

8.6 Summary of the Differences between the Types of Functions

FORTRAN provides for four types of functions: those supplied with the system, arithmetic statement functions, and those established by FUNCTION and SUBROUTINE statements. The differences between them may be summarized as follows.

Naming. The names of supplied and arithmetic statement functions contain four to seven letters or digits, the first of which must be alphabetic and the last F; the first character must be X if and only if the value of the function is fixed point. The name of a FUNCTION subprogram contains one to six letters or digits, the first of which must be I, J, K, L, M, or N if and only if the value of the function is fixed point; the last character must not be F if the name is more than three characters long. The name of a SUBROUTINE subprogram has one to six letters or digits; the first of which must be a letter and the last of which must not be F if the name is more than three characters long.

Definition. Supplied functions are provided with the system (and usually expanded by each installation). Arithmetic statement functions are defined by a single arithmetic statement. A FUNCTION subprogram is defined by any number of statements following a FUNCTION statement. A SUBROUTINE subprogram is defined by any number of statements following a SUBROUTINE statement.

How called into action. Supplied, arithmetic statement, and FUNCTION functions are brought into action by writing the name of the function in an expression where its value is desired. A SUBROUTINE subprogram is brought into action by a CALL statement.

Number of arguments. The number of arguments for supplied functions is specified for each function. Arithmetic statement functions and FUNCTION subprograms may have any number of arguments from *one* to some reasonable maximum. A SUBROUTINE subprogram may have

any number of arguments from *none* to some reasonable maximum.

Number of outputs. A SUBROUTINE subprogram may have any number of outputs, including none, whereas all of the others are restricted to exactly one.

Note. The reader now has adequate background for all Case Studies.

EXERCISES

*1. Define an arithmetic statement function to compute

$$\text{DENOMF(X)} = X^2 + \sqrt{1 + 2X + 3X^2}$$

Then use the function to compute

$$\text{ALPHA} = \frac{6.9 + Y}{Y^2 + \sqrt{1 + 2Y + 3Y^2}}$$

$$\text{BETA} = \frac{2.1Z + Z^4}{Z^2 + \sqrt{1 + 2Z + 3Z^2}}$$

$$\text{GAMMA} = \frac{\sin Y}{Y^4 + \sqrt{1 + 2Y^2 + 3Y^4}}$$

$$\text{DELTA} = \frac{1}{\sin^2 Y + \sqrt{1 + 2\sin Y + 3\sin^2 Y}}$$

2. Define an arithmetic statement function to compute

$$\text{SLGF(A)} = 2.549 \log \left(A + A^2 + \frac{1}{A} \right)$$

Then use the function to compute

$$R = X + \log X + 2.549 \log \left(X + X^2 + \frac{1}{X} \right)$$

$$S = \cos X + 2.549 \log \left(1 + X + (1 + X)^2 + \frac{1}{1 + X} \right)$$

$$T = 2.549 \log \left[(A - B)^3 + (A - B)^6 + \frac{1}{(A - B)^3} \right]$$

$$U = [B(I) + 6]^2 + 2.549 \log \left[\frac{1}{B(I)} + \frac{1}{B(I)^2} + B(I) \right]$$

*3. Define an arithmetic statement function to compute

$$\text{S34F(X,A)} = \sqrt{X^2 - A^2}$$

Then use it to compute

$$\text{SFK} = \frac{V \cdot \sqrt{V^2 - R^2}}{2} - \frac{R^2}{2} \log |V + \sqrt{V^2 - R^2}|$$

$$\text{PSB} = \frac{[X(I)^2 - B^2]^{7/2}}{7} + \frac{2B^2[X(I)^2 - B^2]^{5/2}}{5} + \frac{B^4[X(I)^2 - B^2]^{3/2}}{3}$$

4. Write an arithmetic statement function to compute

$$SQUADF(A,B,C,X) = \sqrt{AX^2 + BX + C}$$

Then use it to compute

$$ETX = \frac{4PZ + 2Q}{(4PR - Q^2)\sqrt{PZ^2 + QZ + R}}$$

$$AVP = \sqrt{RY^2 + SY + \sqrt{DY^2 + EY + 16}}$$

*5. Write a FUNCTION subprogram to compute

$$Y(X) = \begin{cases} 1 + \sqrt{1 + X^2} & \text{if } X < 0 \\ 0 & \text{if } X = 0 \\ 1 - \sqrt{1 + X^2} & \text{if } X > 0 \end{cases}$$

Then write statements to compute the following formulas, which use the mathematical function notation: "Y as a function of A + Z," etc.

$$F = 2 + Y(A + Z)$$

$$G = \frac{Y[X(K)] + Y[X(K + 1)]}{2}$$

$$H = Y[\cos(2\pi X)] + \sqrt{1 + Y(2\pi X)}$$

6. Write a FUNCTION subprogram to compute

$$RHO(A,B,N) = \frac{A}{2\pi}\sum_{i=1}^{N} B_i$$

where B is a one-dimensional array of 50 elements ($N \leq 50$).

Then use it to compute $\frac{1}{2\pi}$ times the sum of the first 18 elements of an array named A; call this SOME.

*7. If A is any two-dimensional array with 20 rows and 20 columns, write a FUNCTION subprogram to get

the sum of the absolute values of the elements in the Kth row of A, except for A(K,K), that is,

$$SUMNR(A,K) = \sum_{j \neq K} |A_{Kj}|$$

Hint. This is the same as $\sum_{\text{all } j} |A_{Kj}| - |A_{KK}|$.

8. A is any 20 by 20 array. Write a FUNCTION subprogram to compute

PD(A,I,J)

$$= \frac{A(I-1, J) + A(I+1, J) + A(I, J-1) + A(I, J+1)}{4}$$

Then use it to compute

$$B_{ij} = (1 - A)B_{ij} + A\frac{B_{i-1,j} + B_{i+1,j} + B_{i,j-1} + B_{i+1,j}}{4}$$

(Could an arithmetic statement function be used here?)

*9. A is a one-dimensional array with a maximum of 50 elements. Write a SUBROUTINE subprogram to compute the average of the first N elements and a count of the number of these elements that are zero. Call the subprogram AVERNZ(A, N, AVER, NZ).

Then use the subprogram to get the average of the first 20 elements of an array named ZETA, place the average in ZMEAN and the count of zero elements in NZCNT.

10. Given single variables A, B, X, and L, write a SUBROUTINE subprogram to compute R, S, and T from

$$R = \sqrt{A + BX + X^L}$$

$$S = \cos(2\pi X + A) \cdot e^{BX}$$

$$T = \left(\frac{A + BX}{2}\right)^{L+1} - \left(\frac{A - BX}{3}\right)^{L-1}$$

9. CASE STUDIES

This chapter contains a number of illustrative problems from various areas of science and engineering. In each there is a statement of the problem, a short discussion of the method of solution, and a complete FORTRAN program, including input and output statements. The problems will not be equally familiar to all readers, but the problem statements do not in any case require specialized knowledge of the subject matter.

These case studies are intended to do two things:

1. To suggest, at least to a small extent, the range of problems which may be attacked with FORTRAN and to illustrate a few of the numerical methods that are frequently used.

2. To illustrate the essential features of FORTRAN itself.

It must always be kept clearly in mind that the use of FORTRAN—or, for that matter, any computer—does not relieve the user of the work of choosing an appropriate mathematical approach to the solution. When a problem is initially posed, it is always necessary to decide what mathematical model most satisfactorily represents the physical problem and then to consider the techniques that will most satisfactorily lead to a solution of the mathematical description. The choice of an appropriate mathematical model belongs to the study of the various problem areas. The choice of an appropriate method of solution of the mathematical system belongs to the realm of numerical analysis. We do not attempt here,

except incidentally, to cover either of these areas.

Case Study 1. Column Design

A mechanical engineer wishes to obtain data for plotting a curve of the safe loading of a certain type of column as a function of the slimness ratio of the column. He has selected from a handbook two empirical formulas that give the safe loading in two ranges of the slimness ratio.

$$S = \begin{cases} 17,000 - 0.485\ R^2 & \text{for } R < 120 \\[2ex] \dfrac{18,000}{1 + \dfrac{R^2}{18,000}} & \text{for } R \geq 120 \end{cases}$$

where S = safe load, pounds/in^2
R = slimness ratio

The safe loading is to be calculated for slimness ratios from 20 through 200, in steps of 5. This range of values can be expressed in the convenient notation:

$$\text{slimness ratio} = 20(5)200$$

This problem can be done without reading any data cards, by writing statements to compute all of the desired values of the slimness ratio. Two IF statements are needed. One will determine which of the two formulas is to be used, and the other will determine when all of the desired values of the slimness ratio have been used. A block diagram is shown in Figure 9.1 and a program in Figure 9.2.

We may review the process required to get answers from the computer. The source program statements shown in Figure 9.2 are punched on cards, with every period and comma exactly as shown. The FORTRAN processor program is then read into the machine from a much larger deck of cards or from magnetic tape. It in turn reads in the source program deck. After a series of computer operations that are not our concern in this text, an object program deck is produced which contains the actual computer instructions to carry out the computation.

It must be realized that the computation has not yet been carried out and no answers have been produced. All that has been accomplished so far is the translation of the FORTRAN statements into machine instructions. With the FORTRAN processor now out of the picture, the object program may be loaded into the computer. It happens that the program for this case study does not call for the reading of cards, but it is at this point that any data cards would be combined with the object program. These cards would be placed behind the object program deck to be read in by the instructions which have been created from the READ statements in the source program. The object program is now

executed, including the reading of data and the printing of results.

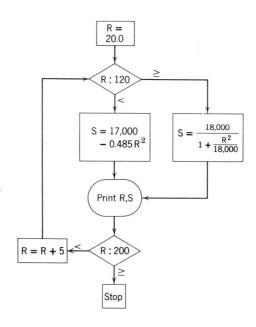

Figure 9.1. Block diagram of the method of solution of Case Study 1.

C FOR COMMENT

STATEMENT NUMBER	Cont.	FORTRAN STATEMENT	
1 5	6	7	72
		R = 20.	
10		IF (R - 120.) 20, 30, 30	
20		S = 1.7E4 - .485*R*R	
		GO TO 40	
30		S = 1.8E4/(1. + R*R/1.8E4)	
40		PRINT 70, R, S	
70		FORMAT (2E20.8)	
		IF (R - 200.) 50, 60, 60	
50		R = R + 5.	
		GO TO 10	
60		STOP	
		END	

Figure 9.2. Program for Case Study 1.

Case Study 2. An Efficiency Calculation

One form of the equation for the theoretical efficiency of a Diesel engine is

$$\text{Eff} = 1 - \frac{1}{R^{\gamma-1}} \left[\frac{\left(\frac{v_3}{v_2}\right)^\gamma - 1}{\gamma\left(\frac{v_3}{v_2} - 1\right)} \right]$$

where R = compression ratio

γ = ratio of specific heats

$\dfrac{v_3}{v_2}$ = load ratio

An engineer wishes to study the variation of efficiency with changes in R and γ, for a fixed value of v_3/v_2. He wishes to be able to run the program several times, perhaps using a different fixed v_3/v_2 and perhaps with different ranges of values of R and γ. Therefore, he has decided to read in a starting value for R, an increment in R, and the desired number of values of R to be used. The same scheme is used for γ. The efficiency is to be calculated for a fixed value of the load ratio and all combinations of R and γ.

The following listing shows the variable names chosen for the program, along with sample values for each variable.

Variable	Variable Name	Sample Value
Load ratio	V	0.163
First compression ratio	R	8.0
Increment in compression ratio	DELR	0.5
Number of compression ratios	NR	21
First specific heat ratio (γ)	G	1.3
Increment in specific heat ratio	DELG	0.05
Number of specific heat ratios	NG	9

This problem can be set up quite easily by using a nest of two DO loops. The outer loop controls the value of R and the inner loop the value of γ. Since the entire inner loop is carried out for each value of R, some way of retaining the initial value of γ must be provided. This is done by using a new variable named GG for γ within the inner loop. Each time the inner loop is started, GG is set equal to G. The program is shown in Figure 9.3.

A problem of this sort, in which a basic computation is carried out for many combinations of values of the independent variables, is often called a *parameter study*.

```
      READ 30, V, R, DELR, NR, G, DELG, NG
   30 FORMAT (3F10.0, I10, 2F10.0, I10)
      DO 21 I = 1, NR
      GG = G
      DO 22 J = 1, NG
      EFF = 1. - 1./R**(GG-1.)*(V**GG -1.)/(GG*(V-1.))
      PRINT 31, V, R, GG, EFF
   31 FORMAT (4F20.8)
   22 GG = GG + DELG
   21 R = R + DELR
      STOP
      END
```

Figure 9.3. Program for Case Study 2.

Case Study 3. Damped Oscillation

The current flowing in a series circuit containing resistance, inductance, and capacitance is given by

$$i = I_m e^{-Rt/2L} \sin 2\pi f_1 t$$

where $I_m = \dfrac{2\pi f_0^2 Q}{f_1}$

$$f_0 = \frac{1}{2\pi} \sqrt{\frac{1}{LC}}$$

$$f_1 = \frac{1}{2\pi} \sqrt{\frac{1}{LC} - \frac{R^2}{4L^2}}$$

and i = current flowing at time t, amperes

I_m = maximum current, amperes

R = resistance, ohms

t = time since closing switch, seconds

L = inductance, henrys

f_0 = frequency of undamped circuit (R = 0), cycles per second

f_1 = frequency of damped circuit, cycles per second

C = capacitance, farads

Q = initial charge on capacitor, coulombs

An electrical engineer wishes to compute a number of points on the curve of instantaneous current versus time, in order to draw a graph. It has been decided that 100 time points will be used and that the spacing between them will be one-tenth of the time required for one complete wavelength at the undamped frequency. In other words, the time interval, named DELT in the program, is $0.1/F_0$.

All of this may be done with a program involving a simple DO loop. The letters appearing in the formulas are used as variable names, except that any names that would otherwise be incorrectly regarded as denoting fixed point variables are written with an A in front. Furthermore, to avoid recomputing the factors R/2L and $2\pi F_1$ every time through the loop, they are computed once at the outset and given the names C_1 and C_2, respectively. The formula thus becomes

$$i = I_m e^{-C_1 t} \sin (C_2 t)$$

where $C_1 = \dfrac{R}{2L}$

$$C_2 = 2\pi f_1$$

The program for this computation could be as shown in Figure 9.4.

```
      27  READ 612, Q, R, C, AL
     612  FORMAT (4F10.0)
          IF (R**2 - 4.*AL/C) 10, 12, 12
      10  F0 = 0.159,2*SQRTF(1./(AL*C))
          F1 = 0.159,2*SQRTF(1./(AL*C) - R**2/(4.*AL**2))
          DELT = 0.1/F0
          AIM = 6.2832*F0**2*Q/F1
          C1 = R/(2.*AL)
          C2 = 6.2832*F1
          T = 0.
          DO 11 J = 1, 100
          AI = AIM * EXPF(-C1*T) * SINF(C2*T)
          PRINT 706, T, AI
     706  FORMAT (2E20.8)
      11  T = T + DELT
          GO TO 27
      12  STOP
          END
```

Figure 9.4. Program for Case Study 3.

```
C FOR COMMENT
STATEMENT NUMBER | Cont. |                    FORTRAN STATEMENT                                    72
1              5 6 7
        READ 16, RHO, THETA
        SGN = 1.0
        SUM = 0.0
        DO 20 I = 1, 40
        AI = I
     0  SUM = SUM + SGN /(2.*AI - 1.)**2
     1     *(RHO/10.)**(2.*AI -1.)
     2     *SINF((2.*AI - 1.)*THETA)
   20   SGN = -SGN
        T = 800./9.8696*SUM
        PRINT 17, RHO, THETA, T
        STOP
   16   FORMAT (2F10.0)
   17   FORMAT (3E20.8)
        END
```

Figure 9.5. Initial program for Case Study 4.

Note that the program first determines whether R^2 is less than $4L/C$, because if it is not the formula shown will not apply and any results would be incorrect. This could happen, of course, only if erroneous data were entered, either by mistakes in writing or punching the data or because of a misunderstanding of the physics of the situation.

Case Study 4.   Heat Transfer

A heat transfer problem involving a semicircular plate has been formulated so as to require evaluating the series

$$T(\rho, \theta) = \frac{800}{\pi^2}\left[\left(\frac{\rho}{10}\right)\sin\theta - \frac{1}{3^2}\left(\frac{\rho}{10}\right)^3\sin 3\theta \right.$$

$$\left. + \frac{1}{5^2}\left(\frac{\rho}{10}\right)^5\sin 5\theta - + \cdots\right]$$

This series converges for $0 \leq \rho \leq 10$ and $0 \leq \theta \leq \pi$ so that there is no problem of convergence in these ranges of ρ and θ. All we have to do is to determine how many terms in the series are required for sufficient accuracy.

The analysis of the error committed by truncating the series after a finite number of terms poses a few slight difficulties. Although the series is absolutely convergent, it is only "approximately" alternating because of the minus sign that is introduced by the sine function. For a first attempt at programming the evaluation of this series, we take a conservative approach and use 40 terms regardless of the size of ρ and θ. This is probably a great deal more than adequate, but we will not worry about the possible waste of computer time for the moment.

We may exhibit this formula in a way that will make it a little bit more obvious how a DO loop can be set up to evaluate it.

$$T(\rho, \theta) = \frac{800}{\pi^2}\sum_{i=1}^{40}\frac{(-1)^{i+1}}{(2i-1)^2}\left(\frac{\rho}{10}\right)^{2i-1}\sin[(2i-1)\theta]$$

It will be necessary to rename the index of summation within the loop to make it a floating point variable and to provide for proper and rapid handling of the $(-1)^{i+1}$ factor. Before going into the DO loop, we set up a constant equal to $+1$ and then reverse its sign after each execution of the DO loop, which is faster than raising to a power.

The program is now easily written, as shown in Figure 9.5. In practice, we would ordinarily compute the temperature at a network of points in the interior of the plate, using two DO loops to work through ranges of values of ρ and θ. However, we understand how this can be done and will not bother with the required statements. We simply read values of ρ and θ and compute the temperature at that particular point.

The programmer who sets up the evaluation of the formula this way is in for a rude shock. He will discover, when he runs the program, that the speed of a computer can be completely wasted by careless problem analysis. The IBM 650, for instance, would require at least half a minute to carry out this computation and much longer if the particular machine did not have built-in floating point. If the temperature actually were desired only at one point, this might not matter; but if it were needed for 200 points the computation would take over an hour on the IBM 650. Bearing in mind that this problem is much simpler than many that are done, it is clear that thought must sometimes be given to speed of execution.

A number of things will improve the speed. To begin with, obviously something must be done to reduce the number of terms computed when a few will suffice. If, for instance, $\rho = 1.0$, then only three terms are required to obtain all the accuracy that makes sense. Even if $\rho = 9.0$, the 20th term is at most about 10^{-4}, regardless of the contribution of the sine function. We clearly need to set up a procedure for stopping the evaluation of the series after the terms have become smaller than some minimum value. This is not precisely correct, of course: in testing the size of a term, we must exclude the sine factor; otherwise we might very well find a term that is almost zero, even though ρ is close to 10. We therefore set up the testing procedure so that it will be carried out before the multiplication of the term by the sine.

A second likely candidate for time reduction is the raising of $\rho/10$ to a power. The procedure used above is particularly bad because we are raising a number to a floating point power. The object program is compiled to use the formula

$$A^B = 10^{B \log A}$$

or

$$A^B = e^{B \ln A}$$

The computation of the exponential and the logarithm are both fairly time-consuming.

```
C FOR COMMENT
STATEMENT NUMBER          FORTRAN STATEMENT
1      5  6 7                                                                72

      10    READ 16, RHO, THETA
            SGN = 1.
            SUM = 0.
            X = RHO/10.
            X2 = X**2
            ANGLE = THETA
            DENOM = 1.
      60    TEST = X/DENOM**2
            SUM = SUM + SGN * TEST * SINF(ANGLE)
            IF (TEST - 1.E-4) 40, 50, 50
      50    X = X * X2
            ANGLE = ANGLE + 2.*THETA
            DENOM = DENOM + 2.
            SGN = -SGN
            GO TO 60
      40    T = 800./9.8696 * SUM
            PRINT 17, RHO, THETA, T
            GO TO 10
      16    FORMAT (2F10.0)
      17    FORMAT (3E20.8)
            END
```

Figure 9.6. Improved version of the program for Case Study 4.

A much better procedure is available, in which $\rho/10$, which we will call X, and $(\rho/10)^2$, which we will call X2, are initially computed. Multiplying the two together gives $(\rho/10)^3$; multiplying this result by X2 gives us $(\rho/10)^5$, etc. This running computation of the next power of $(\rho/10)$ from the previous one is easily set up in a loop, even though it will not be a DO loop now.

Similarly, each new value of the angle in the sine function can be obtained by adding 2θ to the previous value of a variable, which is initially set equal to θ. An equivalent process produces the $1/(2i - 1)^2$ factor.

A somewhat analogous attack could be made on the sine, using the addition formulas for sine and cosine. However, this would be of dubious value.

If we arbitrarily establish the criterion that the evaluation of the series should be stopped as soon as the absolute value of a term (exclusive of the sine factor) becomes less than 10^{-4}, then the program can be as shown in Figure 9.6.

A number of other short cuts could be taken to speed up this program further, but they would not be significant compared with what has already been done. Just to indicate the potential time savings, for all values of ρ less than 8.0 the revised program is at least 20 times as fast as the original one.

Case Study 5.   A Servomechanism Frequency Response Plot

The transfer function of a certain servomechanism is given by

$$T(i\omega) = \frac{K}{i\omega(1 + iT_1\omega)(1 + iT_2\omega)}$$

where ω = angular frequency, radians/second
  $i = \sqrt{-1}$
  T = transfer function
  K = amplification factor
  T_1, T_2 = time constants, seconds

(In electrical engineering work j is usually written for i.)

A mathematician wishes to be able to read in values of K, T_1, and T_2 and to compute the transfer function for a number of values of ω. The transfer function will, in general, be a complex number. The simplest way to handle the complex arithmetic in this case is to rewrite the formula so that the real and imaginary parts are separated.

All arithmetic will then involve only real quantities—which is all we can deal with. The formula for the transfer function now becomes

$$T(i\omega) = \frac{-K(T_1 + T_2)}{(1 - T_1T_2\omega^2)^2 + \omega^2(T_1 + T_2)^2}$$
$$- \frac{K(1 - T_1T_2\omega^2)}{\omega[(1 - T_1T_2\omega^2)^2 + \omega^2(T_1 + T_2)^2]} \cdot i$$

The real and imaginary parts of T are printed for each of a range of values of ω. The program is set up to allow this range to be specified in either of two ways. In addition to the values of K, T_1, and T_2, four other numbers will be read: W, WL, C, and L. T is to be computed first with $\omega = W$. To get each succeeding value of ω, either C is to be *added* to the previous ω, if L = 1, or ω is to be *multiplied* by C, if L = 2. In either case the computation is continued until T has been computed for the largest value of ω not exceeding WL.

The program is shown in Figure 9.7. It may be noted that several intermediate variables were established in the program, in order to avoid computing them more often than necessary. F1 does not depend on ω and is computed only once at the outset. F2 and F3 have to be computed for each value of ω, but we can at least avoid evaluating the expression several times for each ω. We could, in fact, have written the program with the computation proper requiring only two statements, one for the real and one for the imaginary part. This, however, would have produced two very long statements requiring a number of continuation cards, and some of the factors appearing in the computation would have been computed three times. This wastes a little bit of computer time, makes the object program longer than necessary, and somehow offends our sense of how things ought to be done. The use of this type of intermediate variable is recommended.

Case Study 6.   Simultaneous Linear Algebraic Equations

A mathematician wishes to set up a program that will solve any system of simultaneous linear algebraic equations satisfying certain requirements, of two to forty equations in the same number of unknowns. The system must meet the following restriction: the main diagonal coefficient in each

```
C FOR COMMENT
STATEMENT
NUMBER    Cont.
1       5 6 7                    FORTRAN STATEMENT                         72
        READ 1, AK, T1, T2, W, WL, C, L
     1  FORMAT (6F10.0, I10)
        F1 = T1 + T2
    50  F2 = 1.0 - T1*T2*W**2
        F3 = F2**2 + W**2 * F1**2
        TREAL = -AK*F1/F3
        TIMAG = -AK*F2/(W*F3)
        PRINT 2, W, TREAL, TIMAG
     2  FORMAT (3E20.8)
        IF (W - WL) 100, 200, 200
   100  GO TO (101, 102), L
   101  W = W + C
        GO TO 50
   102  W = C * W
        GO TO 50
   200  STOP
        END
```

Figure 9.7. Program for Case Study 5.

row must *dominate* the other coefficients in the row, which is true if

$$|A_{ii}| > \sum_{j \neq i} |A_{ij}|, \qquad i = 1, 2, \cdots, N$$

$$N = \text{number of equations}$$

(Less stringent restrictions are actually sufficient, but a discussion of them is beyond the scope of this text.)

The method to be used for solution, the Seidel iteration method, will find the solution (if there is one, of course) to any system of equations meeting this restriction, but it will be particularly advantageous if either or both of the following additional condititons are satisfied:

1. An approximate solution is known in advance.
2. Most of the coefficients are zero. (If there are special characteristics, such as all zeros above the main diagonal, much better methods are available.)

The essence of the Seidel iteration method is to make a guess at the values of the unknowns and then to improve the guess repeatedly. With the restrictions stated above, the successive approximations will converge to the true values of the un-

knowns, no matter what initial guess is taken. We illustrate the process with a system of three equations and three unknowns.

$$A_{11}X_1 + A_{12}X_2 + A_{13}X_3 = B_1$$
$$A_{21}X_1 + A_{22}X_2 + A_{23}X_3 = B_2$$
$$A_{31}X_1 + A_{32}X_2 + A_{33}X_3 = B_3$$

We begin by making an initial guess at the values of X_1, X_2, and X_3. If there is any information available about the expected values of the unknowns, then such values should be used. The closer the initial guesses to the final values, the fewer the number of iterations that will be required. Lacking such information, we may use any values, typically zero for each variable.

We begin by computing a new value of X_1 from the first equation. With a prime to denote a new value of an unknown, we may write

$$X_1' = (B_1 - A_{12}X_2 - A_{13}X_3)/A_{11}$$

Using this new value of X_1 and the old value of X_3, we compute a new value for X_2 from equation 2:

$$X_2' = (B_2 - A_{21}X_1' - A_{23}X_3)/A_{22}$$

Using the new values of X_1 and X_2, we compute a new value for X_3 from equation 3:

$$X_3' = (B_3 - A_{31}X_1' - A_{32}X_2')/A_{33}$$

This gives us a new approximation to the values of the unknowns, which constitutes one iteration. As many iterations are taken as are required to obtain two successive approximations to the unknowns that are "sufficiently close" to each other. Various definitions of closeness are used; here, on each iteration we will form the sum of the absolute values of the differences between each new value of the unknowns and the previous value of the unknowns. The measure of the difference between two successive sets of unknowns, which is often called the *norm*, is thus given by

$$E = \sum_{i=1}^{N} |X_i' - X_i|$$

What this means in programming terms is that before storing the new value of each unknown we must form the absolute value of the difference between it and the previous value of that unknown and add to the error sum.

At the end of each iteration we will determine whether the error sum is less than a test constant which is read in as input. If it is, then the unknowns have been computed to sufficient accuracy; if not, we must make another iteration.

We must give some thought to how the data should be entered. A system of 40 equations could require entering 1680 numbers: 1600 coefficients, 40 constant terms, and 40 initial approximations. If a particular system has fewer than 40 equations, we, of course, will have fewer numbers to enter, but even 20 equations could involve 440 numbers. This quantity of data requires considerable card preparation effort, and we naturally look for some way to reduce it if possible. The most obvious simplification is to take advantage of the expectation that many of the quantities may be zeros. We will therefore clear the three arrays (coefficients, constants, and unknowns) to zero initially and then read in only the nonzero items.

Since there are three kinds of data that could be entered, we must either provide an identification on each card of the data it contains or group the data cards according to their function. We adopt the latter course. We will assume that all of the coefficient cards will appear at the front of the deck, followed by all of the cards for the con-

stant terms, followed by all of the the cards for the initial guesses for the unknowns. Since we do not know how many quantities there may be in each group, some way must be provided to indicate the end of each group. This may be handled as a part of the scheme for identifying the elements.

Each coefficient card will contain two coefficients, in fields 3 and 6. Field 1 will contain, in fixed point form, the row number of the coefficient in field 3, and field 2 will contain the column number of that coefficient. Columns 4 and 5 will perform the same function for the coefficient in field 6. Field 7 on each coefficient card will contain a fixed point 1, except for the last card on which it will contain a 2. All of the constant terms will then follow, punched one to a card. Each card will contain the equation number (row number) of the constant in the first field and the constant itself in the second field. Field 3 will contain a fixed point 1 on all cards except for the last, on which it will be a 2. Precisely the same procedure will be followed with the cards that enter the initial guesses to the unknowns. In the frequent case in which the initial guesses are all zero it will be necessary to enter only one zero guess and to identify that card as being the last. Since all of the arrays involved will be cleared to zero before the cards are read, any elements that are not entered from cards will be taken to be zero in the computation.

At the front of the deck will be a card that contains the number of equations in field 1 and the value that should be used to test for convergence of the iteration process in field 2.

Although the program shown in Figure 9.8 is slightly longer than others we have seen, it presents no great difficulties. The heart of the iteration is the procedure for evaluating the products in each equation which are used to compute a new value of the unknown from that equation. In the first equation this requires forming the sums of all the terms after the first. In the last equation it involves forming the sums of the products of all the terms before the last. In the general case of an equation that is neither first nor last it involves some products that come before the term containing the unknown being computed and some that come after. It is possible to set up two DO loops and a special procedure for handling the first and last equations, but a simpler solution is available. We can form the sum of all the products in an equation and then subtract the product containing

```
C PROGRAM TO SOLVE N SIMULTANEOUS EQUATIONS IN N
C UNKNOWNS, BY SEIDEL ITERATION METHOD...  N MUST
C NOT EXCEED 40..  ONLY THE NON-ZERO ELEMENTS IN
C ARRAYS NEED BE ENTERED..
      DIMENSION A(40, 40), B(40), X(40)
C CLEAR ARRAYS
      DO 50 I = 1, 40
      B(I) = 0.0
      X(I) = 0.0
      DO 50 J = 1, 40
   50 A(I, J) = 0.0
C READ N AND CONVERGENCE TEST CONSTANT
      READ 20, N, TEST
   20 FORMAT (I2, F10.0)
C READ COEFFICIENTS
   31 READ 21, I, J, (A(I, J)), II, JI, (A(II, JI)), NEXT
   21 FORMAT (2(2I2, F10.0), I1)
      GO TO (31, 32), NEXT
```

```
C READ CONSTANTS
   32 READ 22, I, (B(I)), NEXT
   22 FORMAT (I2, F10.0, I1)
      GO TO (32, 33), NEXT
C READ INITIAL GUESSES
   33 READ 22, I, (X(I)), NEXT
      GO TO (33, 34), NEXT
C START AN ITERATION
   34 ERROR = 0.0
      DO 35 I = 1, N
      SUM = 0.0
      DO 40 J = 1, N
   40 SUM = SUM + A(I, J) * X(J)
   39 TEMPX = (B(I) - SUM + A(I, I) * X(I))/A(I, I)
      ERROR = ERROR + ABSF(X(I) - TEMPX)
   35 X(I) = TEMPX
C END OF ONE ITERATION.  PRINT ERROR AND TEST CONVERGENCE
      PRINT 23, ERROR
   23 FORMAT (E20.8)
      IF (ERROR - TEST) 41, 34, 34
```

Figure 9.8. Program for Case Study 6.

```
C FOR COMMENT
STATEMENT
NUMBER           FORTRAN STATEMENT                                          72
1        5  6 7

C  PUNCH ANSWERS
    41  NEXT1 = 1
        NEXT2 = 2
        NM1 = N - 1
        DO 42 I = 1, NM1
    42  PUNCH 22, I, X(I), NEXT1
        PUNCH 22, N, X(N), NEXT2
        STOP
        END
```

Figure 9.8 (Continued).

the unknown being computed. (This programming convenience will cause loss of significance, however, in unfavorable situations.)

In looking at this program, we note several instructive features. In statement 31 there is an example of variables in the list being used as subscripts later in the list. This is perfectly permissible and, in such cases as this, very valuable. The variable NEXT is the number that is read from each card to indicate whether or not this is the last card in a group. The same variable is used on all of the READ statements.

At statement 39 we calculate the new value of the unknown currently being computed. We note in this statement a variable in which both subscripts are the same fixed point variable. This is perfectly legitimate; what we want here is to obtain the diagonal element from whatever equation we are in, and this subscripting does just that. The statement following 39 adds to the error sum the difference between the new value of the unknown just computed and the old value of that unknown. The absolute value function is used to discard the sign of the difference. After the difference has been added to the error value, we store the new value in the location for the unknown.

Following statement 35, which ends one iteration, we print the value of the error. This is done because the programmer might like to be able to watch the convergence of the unknowns, perhaps stopping the process if convergence is too slow. (Note, however, that this practice is not permitted at many installations.) Following this, we have an IF statement to determine whether the iteration process has converged within the limits set by the value of the variable TEST. If we have fin-

ished, we punch out the values of the unknowns in the same format in which the initial guesses were entered in order to be able to use the deck as input later, if desired. That is to say, we punch the number of the unknown, the unknown itself, and then either a 1 or a 2, depending on whether this is the last card. It should be noted in these punch statements that we had to define a variable for the value of 1 and another one for the value of 2. We recall that the list of an input or output statement can contain only variable names, not constants.

Case Study 7. An Ordinary Differential Equation

A mathematician wishes to integrate the following ordinary differential equation:

$$\frac{dy}{dx} = \sqrt[3]{2x^3 + y^2} + 1.63e^{-(x+y)}$$

where y = 2 when x = 1.

There is no analytical solution, and we immediately turn to numerical methods. This book is not the place to discuss the choice of one method from the many that are available; we select a variation of the Runge-Kutta method, more or less arbitrarily.

As in any numerical attack on an ordinary differential equation, we begin at the known point on the curve and use the equation for the derivative at that point to locate an adjacent point. Stating the problem in more general terms, we are given y' as a function of x and y:

$$y' = f(x, y)$$

together with the initial condition that when $x = x_0$, $y = y_0$. We are to find y for $x = x_0 + h$, $x_0 + 2h$, $\cdots$, where h is a constant interval on the x-axis. Let us now say, in general terms, that we know that $y = y_j$ at a general point $x = x_j$; we are next required to find $y = y_{j+1}$ at a point $x = x_{j+1} = x_j + h$. With the Runge-Kutta method, we shall do this by successively applying the following formulas:

$$k_1 = h[f(x_j, y_j)]$$

$$k_2 = h[f(x_j + h/2, y_j + k_1/2)]$$

$$k_3 = h[f(x_j + h/2, y_j + k_2/2)]$$

$$k_4 = h[f(x_j + h, y_j + k_3)]$$

$$y_{j+1} = y_j + \tfrac{1}{6}(k_1 + 2k_2 + 2k_3 + k_4)$$

The program for this computation will begin by reading the starting values of x and y and the value of h. The computation thereafter is relatively straightforward. We substitute the starting values of x and y into the formulas shown above to compute a new value of y at the point $x_0 + h$. We print these two values. The same formulas are then applied to these new values of x and y. The process is continued until as many points on the curve of y as a function of x have been computed as desired. The largest desired value of x will

also be read in by the starting statement; we call this variable XL.

The only programming problem here is that we must evaluate the given function four times in the computation of the next point on the curve. For the equation given, this will be a fairly long statement that we would prefer not to have to write out four times. Therefore, we shall set up an arithmetic statement function to evaluate the formula. Each time we want to compute the formula we will write function name, DERIVF, followed by parentheses enclosing the actual arguments.

Except for this one feature, the program shown in Figure 9.9 is relatively straightforward. Note that we have left the specification of the initial condition flexible, reading in the starting values of x and y as input.

Case Study 8.   Quadratic Equation Solution

A program is to be set up to solve the quadratic equation $Ax^2 + Bx + C = 0$. The program is to be able to read from tape 2 the coefficients of many such equations—possibly hundreds of them—and to produce an easily readable report showing for each equation the coefficients and the two roots. The roots can be real or complex. A heading is to

```
       C FOR COMMENT
STATEMENT                                    FORTRAN STATEMENT
NUMBER    Cont.
1       5 6 7                                                                    72
      0 DERIVF(X,Y) = H * ((2.*X**3 + Y**2)**.3333
      1   + 1.63 * EXPF(-(X+Y)))
   5 0 READ 12, X, Y, H, XL
   1 2 FORMAT (4F10.0)
   4 0 AK1 = DERIVF(X,Y)
        AK2 = DERIVF(X+H/2., Y+AK1/2.)
        AK3 = DERIVF(X+H/2., Y+AK2/2.)
        AK4 = DERIVF(X+H, Y+AK3)
        Y = Y + (AK1 + 2.*AK2 + 2.*AK3 + AK4)/6.
        X = X + H
        PRINT 13, X, Y
   1 3 FORMAT (2E20.8)
        IF(X - XL) 40, 40, 50
        END
```

Figure 9.9.   Program for Case Study 7.

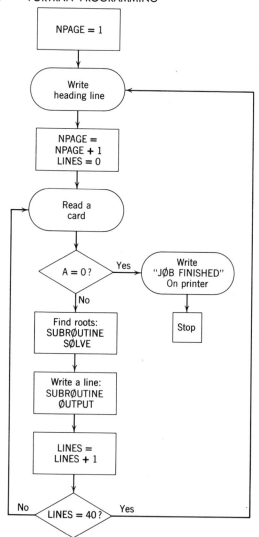

Figure 9.10. Block diagram of the main program for Case Study 8.

be printed at the top of each page, the pages are to be numbered, and the lines are to be counted as they are printed, so that each page will contain only 40 lines of results. The output is to be written on tape 3 for later printing.

The program is to be written to use two SUB-ROUTINE subprograms to make program modification and correction easy. The main routine will handle the reading of data from input tape 2, the printing of page headings, page numbering, line counting, and the detection of the end of the deck, which is signaled by the tape record of blank card, placed at the end of the deck for the purpose. The detection of this card can be set up as a test for a data card in which A = 0. This can never happen with valid data. (If A = 0, the equation is not quadratic.)

The first subprogram will get the solutions, taking into account that if the discriminant $B^2 - 4AC$ is negative, the results will be complex. The input to the subprogram consists of the variables A, B, and C; the output is called X1R, X1I, X2R, and X2I, for the real and imaginary parts of the two roots. These seven variables are named in COMMON statements in the main program and in the two subprograms, so that the SUBROUTINE and CALL statements need no arguments.

The second subprogram writes the coefficients and the results. It is desired to print the results in a way that will indicate to the reader immediately if they are pure real or pure imaginary. If the roots are both real, the space for the imaginary parts is to be left blank, and if they are both pure imaginary the space for the real parts is to be left blank. (We recall that complex roots always occur as complex conjugates; it can never happen that only one root is complex or that the two complex roots have different real parts.)

For this program spacing to a new page after 40 lines of results can be handled by making the first character of the heading line a 1. Obtaining a blank line between the heading and the first line of the results *could* be handled by putting a zero in the first character of the first line of the answers. But this would mean a different FORMAT statement for the first line than for the following lines, which would be a bother. It is simpler, in this case, to call for a blank line by writing two slashes at the end of the FORMAT statement for the heading line.

A block diagram of the main program is shown in Figure 9.10, which is seen to be straightforward. One additional feature has been added: when the blank card at the end of the deck is located, a comment is written on the on-line printer to let the operator know that the final stop has been reached.

The block diagram of the subprogram for finding the roots is shown in Figure 9.11. The procedure shown steers a middle course between the bare minimum required to distinguish between real and complex roots and the more complicated tests that could be made to take advantage of every special situation. The bare minimum would be to go to the complex section if the discriminant is negative and to the real section if it is zero or positive. Since the IF statement automatically gives us a three-way branch, it seems reasonable to take special action if the discriminant is zero, to avoid computing the square root of zero. We could go

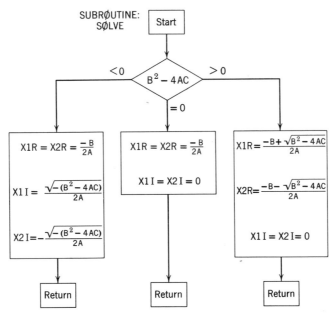

Figure 9.11. Block diagram of the subprogram for finding the roots in Case Study 8.

further with this testing for special conditions, however. If C is zero, then both roots are real, one being zero and the other $-B/A$. If B is zero, then the formulas simplify slightly. If B and C are both zero, then of course both roots are zero—but it is hard to see why such a case would ever be entered.

In any such case it is necessary to draw a line somewhere. Time can indeed be saved in the object program by taking advantage of the special situations—unless testing for them wastes all the savings. It could well be argued that even the amount of testing done here is of dubious value, since it is fairly unlikely that experimental data would ever give a discriminant of exactly zero, to eight places.

The block diagram of the output subprogram, Figure 9.12, is also fairly simple. Note that it is not necessary to test both imaginary components for zero values, since both will always be zero or both nonzero. This is not true of the real parts.

The main program is shown in Figure 9.13. Notice in the first FORMAT statement that the column headings have been spaced out so as to be centered over the columns; the blanks here are essential. The "1" to cause skipping to the top of the next page is included in the counting of printing positions, even though it is not printed. When the blank card is detected, we write an end-of-file mark on the output tape so that the printer operator will know when the end of the output has been

reached and we rewind the two tapes. Then the "JOB FINISHED" message is written on the on-line printer, and the program is stopped. Notice that since all the variables that would have to be transmitted between the main program and the two subprograms are named in a COMMON statement in each place the two CALL statements do not require arguments.

The coding of the two subprograms, shown in Figures 9.14 and 9.15, should not be hard to follow. Two new variables, DISC and S, are set up in the

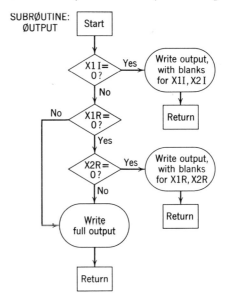

Figure 9.12. Block diagram of the subprogram for printing the results in Case Study 8.

```
       NPAGE = 1
    5  WRITE OUTPUT TAPE 3, 8, NPAGE
   80  FORMAT (114H1         A              B              C              X1
      1REAL          X1 IMAG         X2 REAL        X2 IMAG      PAGE, I4///)
       NPAGE = NPAGE + 1
       LINES = 0
   14  READ INPUT TAPE 2, 15, A, B, C
   15  FORMAT (3F10.5)
       IF (A) 16, 17, 16
   17  END FILE 3
       REWIND 2
       REWIND 3
       PRINT 18
   18  FORMAT (13H JOB FINISHED)
       STOP
   16  CALL SOLVE
       CALL OUTPUT
       LINES = LINES + 1
       IF (LINES - 40) 14, 5, 5
       COMMON A, B, C, X1R, X1I, X2R, X2I
       END
```

Figure 9.13. Main program for Case Study 8.

```
       SUBROUTINE SOLVE
       COMMON A, B, C, X1R, X1I, X2R, X2I
       DISC = B**2 - 4. * A * C
       IF (DISC) 50, 60, 70
   50  X1R = -B/(2.*A)
       X2R = X1R
       X1I = SQRTF(-DISC)/(2.*A)
       X2I = -X1I
       RETURN
   60  X1R = -B/(2.*A)
       X2R = X1R
       X1I = 0.
       X2I = 0.
       RETURN
   70  S = SQRTF(DISC)
       X1R = (-B + S)/(2.*A)
       X2R = (-B   S)/(2.*A)
       X1I = 0.
       X2I = 0.
       RETURN
       END
```

Figure 9.14. Subprogram for finding the roots in Case Study 8.

```
-----C FOR COMMENT
STATEMENT
NUMBER          FORTRAN STATEMENT
1        5  6  7                                                          72

          SUBROUTINE OUTPUT
          COMMON A, B, C, X1R, X1I, X2R, X2I
          IF(X1I) 90, 91, 90
     91   WRITE OUTPUT TAPE 3, 95, A, B, C, X1R, X2R
     95   FORMAT (1H , 1P4E15.4, E30.4)
          RETURN
     90   IF(X1R) 100, 101, 100
    101   IF(X2R) 100, 102, 100
    102   WRITE OUTPUT TAPE 3, 103, A, B, C, X1I, X2I
    103   FORMAT (1H , 1P3E15.4, 2E30.4)
          RETURN
    100   WRITE OUTPUT TAPE 3, 110, A, B, C, X1R, X1I, X2R, X2I
    110   FORMAT (1H , 1P7E15.4)
          RETURN
          END
```

Figure 9.15. Subprogram for printing the results in Case Study 8.

SOLVE subroutine in order to avoid computing certain expressions repeatedly. Advantage is taken of the fact that complex roots occur only as complex conjugates, once again to avoid computing an expression twice.

The program for the OUTPUT subroutine involves no new concepts, but the FORMAT statements should be studied carefully. The blank spaces for the two special cases of pure real and pure imaginary roots are introduced by allowing 15 extra spaces in the appropriate places. Remember that once a scale factor has been given, it applies to all following E and F field specifications until another scale factor appears. The blank first character to give single spacing is entered explicitly with a Hollerith field specification. This could also be done by allowing an extra space for the first field specification, but doing so would require it to be different from the others. The Hollerith method is a little simpler. It is good practice to rewind all tapes *before* using them, to avoid the possibility of a variety of troubles due to improper positioning.

APPENDIX 1. RELATION TO ACTUAL **FORTRAN**-TYPE COMPILERS

As noted in the Introduction on p. 1, the FORTRAN system described in this book differs in some regards from the various actual FORTRAN-type systems in use. Some of these variations are rather minor matters, such as the differences in variable naming, in the sizes of constants, in the form and number of subscripts, in the total length of statements, and in the kind and naming of supplied functions. Other variations are more fundamental, such as the fact that the version of FORTRAN described here has features not found in the smaller systems; these include primarily the FORMAT statement and the three kinds of functions described in Chapter 8. Finally, a few variations are introduced by differences in machine configurations. For instance, FORTRAN for the IBM 650 obviously cannot have a PRINT statement, since the machine has neither a printer nor a typewriter.

Summary of Characteristics of Systems

IBM 1620 FORTRAN

Fixed point constants: 1–4 decimal digits.
Floating point constants: any number of decimal digits; absolute value between 10^{-50} and 10^{49}.
Variable names: 1–5 characters.
Subscripts: a single unsigned fixed point constant or fixed point variable; one- and two-dimensional arrays permitted.
Statements: 72 characters, including blanks; no continuation statements.
Statement numbers: 1–9999.

Functions: all names three characters; argument must be a single variable; no arithmetic statement functions or subprograms.
Input and output: paper tape, typewriter, punched cards; indexing in lists not permitted; naming of entire array without subscripting not permitted; FORMAT statement not used, but input may be in any of the forms permitted for constants.
Statements available: arithmetic, GO TO, computed GO TO, IF, IF (SENSE SWITCH), PAUSE, STOP, DO, CONTINUE, READ, PUNCH, PRINT, DIMENSION.
Remarks: End statement not required.

IBM 1620 GOTRAN

Fixed point constants: 1–3 decimal digits.
Floating point constants: any number of decimal digits; absolute value between 10^{-50} and 10^{49}.
Variable names: fixed point: *one* of the letters I, J, K, L, M, or N; floating point: 1–4 characters, of which the first is not I, J, K, L, M, or N.
Subscripts: a single unsigned fixed point variable; one-dimensional arrays permitted.
Statements: 72 characters, including blanks and a required end-of-statement character; no continuation statements.
Statement numbers: 1–999.
Functions: all names three characters; argument must be a single variable; no arithmetic statement functions or subprograms.
Input and output: paper tape, typewriter, punched cards; list must consist of 1–5 names of single

variables; FORMAT statement not used; input may be any of the forms permitted for constants.

Statements available: arithmetic, GO TO, IF, DO, CONTINUE, PAUSE, STOP, END, READ, PUNCH, PRINT, DIMENSION.

Remarks: GOTRAN is an interpretive system, which means that the source program statements are executed after only a little preliminary processing; no complete object program is ever produced. The source program is interpreted each time the program is run.

IBM 650 FORTRAN

Fixed point constants: 1–10 decimal digits.

Floating point constants: 1–8 decimal digits; absolute value between 10^{-50} and 10^{50}.

Variable names: 1–5 characters.

Subscripts: as described in text; one- and two-dimensional arrays permitted; a maximum of 20 subscripted variables may be used in one program.

Statements: 125 characters, exclusive of blanks; maximum of 9 fixed and floating point constants in any one statement; a nest of DO's may not exceed 4 in depth; at most 25 pairs of parentheses in one statement.

Statement numbers: 1–9999.

Functions: no arithmetic statement functions or subprograms.

Input and output: punched cards; FORMAT statement not used.

Statements available: arithmetic, GO TO, computed GO TO, IF, PAUSE, STOP, DO, CONTINUE, READ, PUNCH, DIMENSION, END.

IBM 650 FOR TRANSIT

Fixed point constants: 1–10 decimal digits.

Floating point constants: 1–8 decimal digits; absolute value between 10^{-50} and 10^{50}.

Variable names: 1–5 characters.

Subscripts: as described in text; one- and two-dimensional arrays permitted; a maximum of 20 subscripted variables may be used in any one program.

Statements: 125 characters, exclusive of blanks; a nest of DO's must not exceed 4 in depth.

Statement numbers: 1–999.

Functions: no arithmetic statement functions or subprograms.

Input and output: punched cards; indexing in lists not permitted; FORMAT statement not used.

Statements available: arithmetic, GO TO, computed GO TO, IF, PAUSE, STOP, DO, CONTINUE, END, READ, PUNCH, DIMENSION, EQUIVALENCE.

Remarks: FOR TRANSIT differs from IBM 650 FORTRAN primarily in the equipment which is required on the computer, together with differences in the operation of the compiler. The EQUIVALENCE statement may refer to subscripted variables only.

IBM 705 FORTRAN

Fixed point constants: 1–10 decimal digits.

Floating point constants: any number of decimal digits; absolute value between 10^{-99} and 10^{99}.

Variable names: 1–10 characters.

Subscripts: as described in text; one-, two-, and three-dimensional arrays permitted.

Statements: maximum of 660 characters, including blanks.

Statement numbers: 1–99999.

Functions: no subprograms.

Input and output: punched cards, attached printer, and magnetic tape; FORMAT statement is required.

Statements available: arithmetic, GO TO, assigned GO TO, ASSIGN, computed GO TO, IF, IF (SENSE SWITCH), STOP, PAUSE, DO, CONTINUE, SENSE LIGHT, IF (SENSE LIGHT), IF ACCUMULATOR OVERFLOW, IF QUOTIENT OVERFLOW, IF DIVIDE CHECK, FORMAT, READ, READ INPUT TAPE, PRINT, WRITE OUTPUT TAPE, END FILE, REWIND, BACKSPACE, PUNCH, DIMENSION, END, READ TAPE, WRITE TAPE.

IBM 7070 FORTRAN

Fixed point constants: 1–10 decimal digits.

Floating point constants: any number of decimal digits; absolute value between 10^{-50} and 10^{50}.

Variable names: 1–6 characters.

Subscripts: essentially as described in text; one-, two-, and three-dimensional arrays permitted.

Statements: maximum of 660 characters including blanks.

Statement numbers: 0–99999.

Functions: essentially as described in text, but no subprograms in basic system.

Input and output: punched cards, typewriter, attached printer, and magnetic tape.

Statements available: arithmetic, GO TO, computed GO TO, assigned GO TO, ASSIGN, IF, SENSE LIGHT, IF (SENSE LIGHT), IF (SENSE SWITCH), IF ACCUMULATOR OVERFLOW, IF QUOTIENT OVERFLOW, IF DIVIDE CHECK, PAUSE, STOP, DO, CONTINUE, FORMAT, READ, READ INPUT TAPE, PUNCH, PRINT, WRITE OUTPUT TAPE, READ TAPE, WRITE TAPE, TYPE, END FILE, REWIND, BACKSPACE, DIMENSION, EQUIVALENCE, FREQUENCY, END; expandable to include SUBROUTINE, FUNCTION, COMMON, CALL, RETURN.

IBM 704/709/7090 FORTRAN

Fixed point constants: 1–5 decimal digits; absolute value less than 32768.

Floating point constants: any number of decimal digits; absolute value between 10^{-38} and 10^{+38}.

Variable names: 1–6 characters.

Subscripts: essentially as described in text; one-, two-, and three-dimensional arrays permitted.

Statements: maximum of 660 characters including blanks.

Statement numbers: 1–32767.

Functions: as described in text.

Input and output: punched cards, attached printer, magnetic tapes.

Statements available: arithmetic, GO TO, assigned GO TO, ASSIGN, computed GO TO, IF, SENSE LIGHT, IF (SENSE LIGHT), IF (SENSE SWITCH), IF ACCUMULATOR OVERFLOW, IF QUOTIENT OVERFLOW, IF DIVIDE CHECK, PAUSE, STOP, DO, CONTINUE, FORMAT, READ, READ INPUT TAPE, PUNCH, PRINT, WRITE OUTPUT TAPE, READ TAPE, READ DRUM, WRITE TAPE, WRITE DRUM, END FILE, REWIND, BACKSPACE, DIMENSION, EQUIVALENCE, FREQUENCY, END.

HONEYWELL ALGEBRAIC COMPILER

Fixed point constants: 1–5 decimal digits, absolute value less than 2^{44}.

Floating point constants: 2–16 characters; absolute value between the approximate limits of 10^{-77} and 10^{+76}.

Variable names: 1–6 characters.

Subscripts: essentially as described in text; one-, two-, and three-dimensional arrays permitted.

Statements: maximum of 660 characters including blanks.

Statement numbers: 1–32767.

Functions: essentially as described in text; arithmetic statement functions are permitted.

Input and output: punched cards, attached printer, typewriter, and magnetic tapes; FORMAT statement is used, except for the typewriter.

Statements available: arithmetic, GO TO, computed GO TO, assigned GO TO, ASSIGN, IF, IF PARITY, IF END OF FILE, SENSE LIGHT, IF (SENSE LIGHT), IF (SENSE SWITCH), IF ACCUMULATOR OVERFLOW, IF QUOTIENT OVERFLOW, IF DIVIDE CHECK, DO, CONTINUE, PAUSE, STOP, TITLE, END, FINIS, FORMAT, READ, READ ONE, READ TWO, PRINT, PRINT ONE, PRINT TWO, PUNCH, PUNCH ONE, PUNCH TWO, READ INPUT TAPE, WRITE OUTPUT TAPE, WRITE TAPE, READ TAPE, END FILE, REWIND, BACKSPACE, ERASE, BUFFER, FUNCTION, SUBROUTINE, CALL, RETURN, DIMENSION, EQUIVALENCE, COMMON.

Remarks: Interspersed machine language symbolic instructions and operations in Boolean algebra are permitted. Several additional types of field specifications are permitted: alphabetic, octal, and blank. Two additional types of variables are allowed: alphabetic and Boolean. A number of differences in the internal operation of the computer are based on the fact that the Honeywell 800 has the ability to run as many as eight programs simultaneously.

PHILCO 2000 ALTAC

Fixed point constants: 1–5 decimal digits; absolute value less than 32768.

Floating point constants: any number of decimal digits; absolute value between 10^{-600} and 10^{600}; an exponent following the significant digits may be as large as 600.

Variable names: 1–7 characters.

Subscripts: any expression representing an integer

quantity; variables in a subscript may themselves be subscripted to any depth; zero and negative subscripts are permitted; one-, two-, three-, and four-dimensional arrays permitted.

Statements: length unlimited; must be terminated by a $; card format for statements somewhat different from that described in text; compound statements are permitted: this is equivalent to writing several statements on one line —they must be separated by semi-colons; mixed expressions containing both fixed and floating point variables are permitted; method of indicating comment cards is different; method of indicating continuation cards is different.

Statement numbers: 1–5 decimal digits or letters.

Functions: essentially as described in text except for slight differences in naming.

Input and output: punched cards, paper tape, attached printer, magnetic tape; FORMAT statement is required.

Statements available: arithmetic, GO TO, computed GO TO, assigned GO TO, ASSIGN, IF, DO, SENSE LIGHT, IF (SENSE LIGHT), IF (SENSE SWITCH), CONTINUE, STOP, PAUSE, IF OVERFLOW, DIMENSION, EQUIVALENCE, READ, PUNCH, READ PAPER TAPE, WRITE PAPER TAPE, READ INPUT TAPE, WRITE OUTPUT TAPE, PRINT, READ TAPE, WRITE TAPE, READ DRUM, WRITE DRUM, BACKSPACE, END FILE, REWIND, SUBROUTINE, FUNCTION, CALL, RETURN, COMMON, END.

Remarks: As may be noted from this summary, ALTAC is considerably different from FORTRAN. Nevertheless, it is compatible with FORTRAN; that is, with rather minor modifications, a FORTRAN program can be compiled with ALTAC. Many of the statements in this text regarding FORTRAN are too restrictive when applied to ALTAC; for example, expressions containing both fixed and floating point variables *are* permitted, as are negative subscripts. Furthermore, there are a number of additional features not present in FORTRAN, such as a more general form of the IF statement and a number of additional types of permitted fields in input and output.

Control Data 1604 FORTRAN

Fixed point constants: 1–14 decimal digits, except when used as an index in a DO loop, where the limit is 5 decimal digits.

Floating point constants: 1–14 decimal digits; absolute value between 10^{-308} and 10^{+308}.

Variable names: 1–7 characters.

Subscripts: essentially as described in text; one-, two-, and three-dimensional arrays permitted.

Statements: maximum of 10 cards.

Statement numbers: 1–9999.

Functions and subroutines: essentially as described in text; subroutines are either obtained from a library tape or can be compiled by the use of FUNCTION and SUBROUTINE statements.

Input and Output: punched cards, attached printer, typewriter, paper tape, magnetic tape; FORMAT statement is required.

Statements available: arithmetic, GO TO, ASSIGN, assigned GO TO, computed GO TO, IF, SENSE LIGHT, IF (SENSE LIGHT), IF (SENSE SWITCH), IF ACCUMULATOR OVERFLOW, IF QUOTIENT OVERFLOW, IF DIVIDE CHECK, PAUSE, STOP, DO, CONTINUE, FORMAT, READ, READ INPUT TAPE, PUNCH, PRINT, WRITE OUTPUT TAPE, READ TAPE, WRITE TAPE, READ DRUM, WRITE DRUM, END FILE, REWIND, BACKSPACE, FUNCTION, SUBROUTINE, RETURN, CALL, DIMENSION, COMMON, EQUIVALENCE, END.

Remarks: Interspersed machine language symbolic instructions are permitted; operations in Boolean algebra are permitted. A large variety of field specifications are permitted in the FORMAT and read/write statements.

APPENDIX 2. STATEMENT SEQUENCING AND PUNCTUATION

The first executable statement in a program is always executed first; control thereafter proceeds sequentially unless modified by DO sequencing or an IF statement. The statements FORMAT, DIMENSION, EQUIVALENCE, and COMMON are *nonexecutable*. In questions of sequencing they can be ignored; they must not be the first statement in the range of a DO.

Statement	Sequencing
a = b	Next executable statement
GO TO n	Statement n
GO TO n, $(n_1, n_2, \cdots, n_m)$	Statement last assigned to n
ASSIGN i TO n	Next executable statement
GO TO $(n_1, n_2, \cdots, n_m)$, i	Statement n_i
IF (e) n_1, n_2, n_3	If $e < 0$, n_1
	$e = 0$, n_2
	$e > 0$, n_3
PAUSE or PAUSE n	Next executable statement
STOP or STOP n	Terminates execution of object program
DO n i = m_1, m_2	DO sequencing, then next executable statement after n
or	
DO n i = m_1, m_2, m_3	
CONTINUE	Next executable statement
END	Primarily a signal to the compiler, but also terminates execution of object program
CALL Name $(a_1, a_2, \cdots, a_n)$	First statement of subroutine named
SUBROUTINE Name $(a_1, a_2, \cdots, a_n)$	Next executable statement
FUNCTION Name $(a_1, a_2, \cdots, a_n)$	Next executable statement
RETURN	The statement following CALL
READ n, List	Next executable statement
READ INPUT TAPE i, n, List	Next executable statement
PUNCH n, List	Next executable statement
PRINT n, List	Next executable statement
WRITE OUTPUT TAPE i, n, List	Next executable statement
FORMAT (Specification)	Not executed
READ TAPE i, List	Next executable statement
WRITE TAPE i, List	Next executable statement
END FILE i	Next executable statement
REWIND i	Next executable statement
BACKSPACE i	Next executable statement
DIMENSION v, v, v, $\cdots$	Not executed
EQUIVALENCE (a, b, c, $\cdots$), (d, e, f, $\cdots$), $\cdots$	Not executed
COMMON A, B, $\cdots$	Not executed

ANSWERS TO SELECTED EXERCISES

There are several acceptable answers to many of the exercises. The one shown here is sometimes "better" than other possibilities, but there is sufficient space to define the criterion of "goodness" for only a few exercises. In other cases, there are several equally "good" answers; for instance, it makes no difference whether one writes $A = B + C$ or $A = C + B$. In short, the answers given here are correct, but not ordinarily unique. If another answer can be shown to be equivalent it must be accepted, unless additional criteria are provided.

CHAPTER 1

2. 12,345.0 (comma not permitted); +234 (no decimal point); 1.6E63 (exponent too large—acceptable in ALTAC); 1E-7 (no decimal point).

3. Yes

5. a. X+Y**3
d. A+B/C
f. A+B/(C+D)
h. ((A+B)/(C+D))**2+X**2
j. 1.+X+X**2/2.+X**3/6.
k. (X/Y)**(G−1.0)

6. b. (X+2.0)/(Y+4.0). Constants may be written in any other equivalent form, such as (X + 2.)/(Y + 4.)
e. ((X+A+3.1416)/(2.0*Z))**2
g. (X/Y)**(R−1.)
j. A+X*(B+X*(C+D*X))

7. c. (A+X)*B/Y
f. (A+B+C*D**2)/(((A+2.8)**(I−1)+B/(C+D))*(A+6.))

CHAPTER 2

2. a. 13, floating
b. zero, floating (same if fixed)
e. 4, fixed

f. 4, floating
k. 0.99999999, floating
n. 8.0, floating (could come out 7.9999999 **or** 8.0000001)
o. 5, fixed

3. a. AREA = 2.*P*R*SINF(3.1416/P)
c. ARC = 2.*SQRTF(Y**2+1.3333*X**2) or ARC = 2.*(Y*Y+4.*X*X/3.)**0.5
e. S = −COSF(X)**(P+1.)/(P+1.)
g. G = 0.5*LOGF((1.+SINF(X))/(1.−SINF(X)))
Preferably written as two statements to avoid computing the sine function twice.
S = SINF(X)
G = 0.5*LOGF((1.+S)/(1.−S))
i. E = X*ATANF(X/A)−A/2.*LOGF(A**2+X**2)
l. Q = (2./(3.1416*X))**0.5*SINF(X). Since $(2/X)^{1/2}(1/\pi)^{1/2} = \sqrt{2/\pi} \cdot 1 \sqrt{X} = 0.7978/\sqrt{X}$, this can be written more compactly (and requiring less time in the object program) as
Q = 0.7978/SQRTF(X)*SINF(X)
n. Y = 2.5065*X**(X+1.)*EXPF(−X)

CHAPTER 3

1.
```
      READ 29, A, B, C
   29 FORMAT (3F10.0)
      S = (A+B+C)/2.
      AR = SQRTF(S*(S−A)*(S−B)*(S−C))
      PRINT 28, A, B, C, S, AR
   28 FORMAT (5E20.8)
```

4.
```
      READ 411, A, E, H, P
      X = E*H*P/(SINF(A)*(H**4/16.+(H*P)**2))
      PRINT 209, A, E, H, P, X
  411 FORMAT (4F10.0)
  209 FORMAT (5E20.8)
```

6.
```
  101 FORMAT (3F10.0)
  402 FORMAT (5E20.8)
      READ 101, A, X, S
      Y = SQRTF(X**2−A**2)
      Z = 0.5*(X*S−A*A*LOGF(ABSF(X+S)))
      PRINT 402, A, X, S, Y, Z
```

CHAPTER 4

1.
```
        IF(X −Y) 11, 11, 12
     11 BIG = Y
        GO TO 13
     12 BIG = X
     13 Continuation of program
```

4.
```
    400 IF(THETA−6.2832) 402, 401, 401
    401 THETA = THETA − 6.2832
        GO TO 400
    402 Continuation
```

5.
```
        IF(ABSF(XREAL)−1.) 16, 82, 82
     16 IF(ABSF(XIMAG)−1.) 81, 82, 82
```

8a.
```
        IF(X − 0.999) 67, 63, 21
     21 IF(X−1.001) 63, 63, 67
```

8b.
```
        IF(ABSF(X−1.)−0.001) 63, 63, 67
```

9.
```
        IF(I−1) 297, 6, 297
      6 IF(R−S) 261, 257, 257
```

12.
```
        X = 1.0
     61 Y = 16.7*X+9.2*X**2−1.02*X**3
        PRINT 62, X, Y
     62 FORMAT(2E20.8)
        IF(X−9.9) 63, 64, 64
     63 X = X+0.1
        GO TO 61
     64 Continuation
```

CHAPTER 5

1.
```
        DIMENSION X(3)
        DIST = SQRTF(X(1)**2+X(2)**2+X(3)**2)
```

3.
```
        DIMENSION A(2,2),C(2,2),B(2,2)
        C(1,1) = A(1,1)*B(1,1)+A(1,2)*B(2,1)
        C(1,2) = A(1,1)*B(1,2)+A(1,2)*B(2,2)
        C(2,1) = A(2,1)*B(1,1)+A(2,2)*B(2,1)
        C(2,2) = A(2,1)*B(1,2)+A(2,2)*B(2,2)
```

5.
```
        DIMENSION A(30), B(30)
        I = 1
        D = 0.
    456 D = D+(A(I)−B(I))**2
        IF(I−30) 457, 458, 458
    457 I = I+1
        GO TO 456
    458 D = SQRTF(D)
```

6.
```
        DIMENSION X(50), DX(49)
      4 I = 1
      9 DX(I) = X(I+1)−X(I)
        IF(I−49) 12, 14, 14
     12 I = I+1
        GO TO 9
     14 Continuation
```

9.
```
        DIMENSION Y(50)
        S = Y(I)+U*(Y(I+1)−Y(I−1))/2.+
        U**2/2.*(Y(I+1)−2.*Y(I)+Y(I−1))
```

11.
```
        DIMENSION A(7), B(7)
     21 FORMAT (7F10.0)
        READ 21, A
        READ 21, B
        I = 1
```

```
        SUM = 0.0
      4 SUM = SUM+A(I)*B(I)
        I = I+1
        IF(I−7) 4, 4, 5
      5 ANORM = SQRTF(SUM)
        PUNCH 22, ANORM
     22 FORMAT (E20.8)
```

CHAPTER 6

1.
```
        DIMENSION AX4(50)
        ASUM = 0.0
        DO 500 I = 1, 50
    500 ASUM = ASUM+AX4(I)
```

3.
```
        DIMENSION M(20)
        DO 43 I = 1, 20
     43 M(I) = I*M(I)
```

5.
```
        DIMENSION R(40), S(40), T(40)
        DO 3 I = 1, M
      3 T(I) = R(I)+S(I)
```

7.
```
        DIMENSION F(50)
        ML1 = M − 1
        DO 6 I = 2, ML1
      6 F(I) = (F(I−1)+F(I)+F(I+1))/3.
```

8.
```
        DIMENSION B(50)
        BIGB = B(1)
        NBIGB = 1
        DO 40 I = 2, 50
        IF(BIGB−B(I)) 60, 40, 40
     60 BIGB = B(I)
        NBIGB = I
     40 CONTINUE
```

10.
```
        DIMENSION X(50), Y(50)
        IF(XT−X(1)) 4190, 100, 100
    100 DO 200 I = 1, 50
        IF(XT−X(I)) 300, 400, 200
    200 CONTINUE
        GO TO 4190
    400 YT = Y(I)
        GO TO 500
    300 YT = Y(I−1)+(Y(I)−Y(I−1))/(X(I)
            −X(I−1))*(XT−X(I−1))
    500
```

12.
```
        DIMENSION A(15,15), X(15), B(15)
        DO 61 I = 1, 15
        B(I) = 0.
        DO 61 J = 1, 15
     61 B(I) = B(I)+A(I,J)*X(J)
```

14.
```
        DIMENSION RST(20,20)
        DPROD = RST(1,1)
        DO 1 I = 2,20
      1 DPROD = DPROD*RST(I,I)
```

15.
```
        X = 1.00
        DO 234 I = 1, 201
        Y = 41.926*SQRTF(1. + X**3) + X**
        .3333*EXPF(X)
        PUNCH 91, X, Y
     91 FORMAT (2E20.8)
    234 X = X + 0.01
```

CHAPTER 7

1.   READ 237, BOS, EWR, PHL, DCA
    237 FORMAT (4F8.0)
        Since all numbers have a decimal point, the
        "0" position in F8.0 is immaterial.

4.   READ 12, LGA, IDL, BAL, ATL
    12 FORMAT (2I3, 2E14.7)
        The "7" position in 2E14.7 is immaterial since
        decimal point is punched.

5.   READ 61, N, (DATA(I), I = 1,N)
    61 FORMAT (I2,10F7.0)

7.   DIMENSION M(3,4)
        READ 1239, M
    1239 FORMAT (12I3)
        M(1,1), M(2,1), M(3,1), M(1,2), M(2,2),
        M(3,2), M(1,3), M(2,3), M(3,3), M(1,4),
        M(2,4), M(3,4)

9.   PRINT 66, A, B, X, Z
    66 FORMAT (2F12.4, 2E20.8)

11.   DIMENSION ABC(10,4)
        WRITE OUTPUT TAPE 3, 123
    123 FORMAT (11H1 MATRIX ABC)
        WRITE OUTPUT TAPE 3, 124 ((ABC(I,J),
            J = 1,4), I = 1,10)
    124 FORMAT (4E20.8)
        Since the closing parenthesis of a FORMAT
        statement always indicates the end of a record
        (printed line, in this case), only four numbers
        will be printed per line.

13.   14 FORMAT (2I2, 1PE20.7)
        DIMENSION PHX(10,13)
        DO 13 I = 1, M
        DO 13 J = 1, N
    13 PUNCH 14, I, J, (PHX(I,J))

CHAPTER 8

1.   DENOMF(X) = X**2+SQRTF(1.+2.*X+
        3.*X**2)
        ALPHA = (6.9+Y)/DENOMF(Y)
        BETA = (2.1*Z+Z**4)/DENOMF(Z)
        GAMMA = SINF(Y)/DENOMF(Y**2)
        DELTA = 1./DENOMF(SINF(Y))

3.   S34F(X,A) = SQRTF(X**2−A**2)
        SFK = 0.5*(V*S34F(V,R) − R**2*LOGF(ABSF
        (V+S34F(V,R))))
        PSB = S34F(X(I),B)**7/7.+2.*B**2*S34F
        (X(I),B)**5/5.+B**4*S34F(X(I),B)**3/3.
        Better in both cases to use two statements: the
        first to compute the function, the second to evalu-
        ate the formula.

5.   FUNCTION Y(X)
        IF(X) 10, 11, 12
    10 Y = 1.+SQRTF(1.+X*X)
        RETURN
    11 Y = 0.
        RETURN
    12 Y = 1.−SQRTF(1.+X*X)
        RETURN
        END
        F = 2.+Y(A+Z)
        G = (Y(X(K))+Y(X(K+1)))/2.
        H = Y(COSF(6.2832*X))+SQRTF(1.+
        Y(6.2832*X))

7.   FUNCTION SUMNR(A,K)
        DIMENSION A(20,20)
        SUMNR = 0.
        DO 69 I = 1, 20
    69 SUMNR = SUMNR + ABSF(A(K,I))
        SUMNR = SUMNR − ABSF(A(K,K))
        RETURN
        END

9.   SUBROUTINE AVERNZ(A,N,AVER,NZ)
        DIMENSION A(50)
        AVER = 0.
        NZ = 0
        DO 19 I = 1,N
        AVER = AVER+A(I)
        IF(A(I)) 19, 18, 19
    18 NZ = NZ+1
    19 CONTINUE
        AN = N
        AVER = AVER/AN
        RETURN
        END
        CALL AVERNZ(ZETA,20,ZMEAN,NZCNT)

INDEX